Dangerousness:
Problems of Assessment and Prediction

Dangerousness:

Problems of Assessment and Prediction

Edited by

John W. Hinton

University of Glasgow

London
GEORGE ALLEN & UNWIN
Boston   Sydney

George Allen & Unwin (Publishers) Ltd,
40 Museum Street, London WC1A 1LU, UK

George Allen & Unwin (Publishers) Ltd,
Park Lane, Hemel Hempstead, Herts HP2 4TE, UK

Allen & Unwin, Inc.,
9 Winchester Terrace, Winchester, Mass 01890, USA

George Allen & Unwin Australia Pty Ltd,
8 Napier Street, North Sydney, NSW 2060, Australia

First published in 1983

British Library Cataloguing in Publication Data

Dangerousness: problems of assessment and prediction.
  1. Crime and criminals – Great Britain
2. Social control
I. Hinton, John W.
364.4'4   HV6795.G7
ISBN 0-04-364021-4

Library of Congress Cataloging in Publication Data

Main entry under title:
Dangerousness: problems of assessment and prediction.
  Includes bibliographical references and index.
1. Violence – Prediction. 2. Insane, Criminal and dangerous.
3. Indeterminate sentence. I. Hinton, John W. (John Wallace)
RC569.5.V55D36 1983   364.3   82-13911
ISBN 0-04-364021-4

Set in 10 on 11 point Times by Fotographics (Bedford) Ltd
and printed in Great Britain by
Biddles Ltd, Guildford, Surrey

Contents

Preface

This book aims to fill a gap in the literature on criminality, particularly in the British publications, by presenting mainly psychological approaches to the assessment and prediction of dangerousness. However, it does not ignore the current moral dilemmas and actual practice of indeterminate detention, and these it discusses first. Lack of space makes full consideration of sociological viewpoints impossible. The disconcerting account of psychiatric labelling procedures and their implications in the United States by the sociologist Stephen Pfohl (1977) provides complimentary reading for this volume. The complete book on Dangerous Offenders in the USA, edited by Conrad and Dinitz (1977), and also the more general volume on the biology of crime edited by Jeffery (1979) could provide useful background to this book.

There is a bias towards psychology in this book because most texts referring to the problem of 'dangerousness' have had either a sociological or a psychiatric bias, and the needs and interests of applied psychologists seem not to have been adequately catered for. While tending towards psychological approaches, the author despairs at the prospect of further inflaming the extensive interdisciplinary conflict in the approach to criminality. In particular, fears of 'social engineering' and dominance by psychologists may be generated in some sociologists by a number of chapters in this book. However, the many-faceted approaches of psychologists can be linked to the data and theoretical approaches of sociologists in predictive studies. Such studies could help us to explain the incidence of different types of violent behaviour.

Having worked in a security hospital and observed the perplexity of patients who plead for some understanding of their condition (for example, why they are labelled 'psychopath'), and seen the despair of those asking for objective assessment and treatment, I feel a real concern for those incarcerated indeterminately. I believe that scientific endeavour to improve assessment, treatment and prediction of behaviour in this field is morally justified, and I am appalled at the barriers facing such research. Despite the rather bleak outlook – or perhaps because of it – I felt this book had to be put together. Hopefully, the scientific contributions will provide pointers to potentially useful areas of research and indicate where some interdisciplinary collaboration is possible.

If the book is not seen as a whole, it is possible that theorists who adopt the social causation theory of crime may be alarmed by the suggestions of implication of physiological factors. However, even the chapter on biochemical aspects recognises a social-developmental interaction with the neuroendocrine system. Socio-biological interaction may eventually be understood better in the causation of behaviour defined as 'dangerous' with the adoption of more advanced statistical techniques for predictive studies. However, the problems of defining 'dangerousness' and the adequacy and justice of present methods of labelling and indeterminate hospitalisation loom heavily over any research endeavour.

I would like to take this opportunity of thanking my fellow contributors who, I know, are united in their concern for the welfare of offenders and the desire for social justice.

JOHN W. HINTON

Acknowledgements

As editor of this book I wish to thank my co-authors for their co-operation and support in compiling this volume for publication. A special 'thank-you' is due to Eileen Graham, without whose dedicated and long-suffering secretarial support this book would never have materialised. Thanks also to Marian Fordom and Alex Crawford for assistance in proof-reading and the provision of helpful comments.

Acknowledgement is made of the assistance and facilities provided by the Departments of Psychology and Forensic Medicine of the University of Glasgow.

This book was completed while the editor was in receipt of a grant from the Social Science Research Council.

Disclaimer

The views expressed in this volume by the invited contributors must not be taken as necessarily reflecting those of any government department or institution – or the views of the editor!

1 Ethics, Theory, Research and Practice: An Overview

JOHN W. HINTON

The first part of this book deals with some of the main ethical, political and professional problems surrounding the indeterminate detention of abnormal and violent offenders – bearing in mind both our present state of knowledge and the evidence available on current practice. By 'abnormal and violent offenders' I am referring specifically here to those deemed suitable for indeterminate detention in mental hospitals, following behaviour judged to be extremely dangerous for society. These individuals may range from those who have committed rape and murder, to people who have thrown stones through the window of the Prime Minister's residence or attacked royalty.

One reason why the debate on 'dangerousness' has become more intense of late is because of moves towards a general reduction in the length of prison sentences. This has led to a greater demand for the use of indeterminate detention in extreme cases, on the grounds of public protection. Some people have argued that 'dangerousness' is not a valid or necessary concept. There is indeed a considerable problem of definition, which is extensively discussed by Professor Nigel Walker in Chapter 3. However, in the minds of most politicians and judges there is little doubt of the reality of this concept, and of the need to label and detain certain people for the protection of society. This in turn raises problems of the adequacy of decision-making. When should indeterminate detention be used? Where should the line be drawn between a 'normal' criminal and a 'dangerous' one? How valid and reliable are the decision-making processes? At the present time the views of the medical profession are sought and powers are vested in the hands of psychiatrists. In reality, psychiatrists may be given the ultimate power of judge and jury in deciding both admission and discharge from places of indeterminate detention. These decisions are based on the extent of diagnosed abnormality of 'mental state', but how fallible are these 'experts'? How scientific are their criteria in making what, for the most part, are *post hoc* decisions of 'mental state' and 'dangerousness'? To what extent should psychiatrists be involved when the *true* issue is 'dangerousness' and not 'mental disorder'?

The shortcomings of the present law and its application to dangerous offenders have been illustrated by a number of well-documented studies. Professor Bottoms has already argued the libertarian viewpoint on the problem of indeterminate detention of so-called 'dangerous' offenders, this argument being based on empirical evidence (Bottoms, 1977). He has quoted a number of important investigations in support of his argument that there is gross overprediction of 'dangerousness' and hence considerable injustice in the use of indeterminate sentences. In this current book he and co-author Roger Brownsword, an expert in jurisprudence, argue the same issue from a philosophical standpoint. The same libertarian conclusions are reached by the logical application of a new ethical approach – a recently developed theory of human rights. As a result of their lucid arguments, these writers do not favour special sentences for the dangerous, except in a very few wholly unusual cases.

After a serious consideration of the problem of the definition of 'dangerousness', Professor Walker provides a somewhat contrasting view to that of Professor Bottoms and Roger Brownsword, with emphasis on the need for 'protecting people'. He recognises that people are generally not improved by long sentences, but that long sentences serve to protect the public from the offender. After dealing with the retributionist argument, he discusses the view that nobody should ever be classified as 'dangerous', and he argues that while it is regrettable that someone should be held in detention who would not reoffend, it is not necessarily morally wrong.

Professor Walker usefully identifies the question of the 'one-off' offender (frequently the domestic murderer, later referred to by psychologist contributors to this volume). Currently, such offenders are among those indeterminately detained in security hospitals for the greatest periods of time. Professor Walker is concerned to ensure safeguards in the making of decisions on what he calls 'protective sentences'. It is suggested that when a court is considering a 'protective sentence' the case should be referred to a special tribunal responsible to the courts. He proposes a system of clear rules to be applied by these tribunals. In this regard he dismisses 'arithmetic rules' in decision-making and he puts forward a series of general non-arithmetic ones.

On the important question of release date for 'protective sentence' offenders, he again proposes the use of a specialist tribunal or a parole board of non-legally qualified experts. He suggests that a system of automatic regular review could be instituted. Regarding 'mentally ill' dangerous offenders committed to hospitals, he considers that the same system could be applied. It is suggested that the review body should include legal, psychiatric and social work representation. He expresses concern about the power of psychiatric opinion on the proposed review body and he suggests a method of restricting this.

Professor Walker's concern about the use of arithmetical rules in decision-making is a fundamental one relating to later sections of this book. The usefulness of various psychological test methods and the quantification of physiological and social data is considered by a number of contributors, as indeed is the concern about the power of psychiatric opinion. While the second and third chapters address the problem of indeterminate detention in general, discussion in these two chapters is relevant to compulsory hospitalisation in particular, and sets the scene for the later chapters.

The 'danger' resulting from the powerful position of psychiatrists in decision-making on indeterminate detention is fully illustrated in the chapter by Dr Treves Brown, himself a consultant psychiatrist with research experience of maximum security hospitals. He reviews widely the scattered literature on compulsory hospital admission and the 'doctor's dilemmas' concerning this problem. The results of his study on the characteristics of offenders referred to the health authority are given, and he compares those whom psychiatrists have chosen to admit, with those not admitted to security hospitals. His analysis of the data shows that commitment of offenders to Special Hospitals depends quite strongly on a number of random factors, and he suggests that doctors are applying some non-medical criteria in making their decisions. Furthermore, he proposes that the data shows how the expectations and attitudes of a few people can have a major influence on rates of referral and admission to maximum security hospitals. The evidence provided by the studies of Dr Treves Brown clearly gives some cause for disquiet: should non-medical factors be considered in coming to a clinical decision? But then, if we consider the haphazard and unscientific nature of the diagnosis of 'psychopathy' as illustrated by Dr Treves Brown in his 1977 paper 'Who is the psychopath?' current medical diagnostic practice itself gives cause for disquiet.

Part 2 of the book consists of a consideration of the methods which are employed, largely by psychologists, in the assessment and treatment of 'dangerous' offenders in security hospital and in prison.

Personality theory underlying the application of psychometrics to dangerous offenders is discussed by Dr Ronald Blackburn, a Consultant Clinical Psychologist with extensive experience of working and researching in two large security hospitals in England. He points out the problems of prediction on the basis of statistical criteria and clinical judgement. Recent advances in psychometric methods which predict dispositions to general aggressive behaviour are discussed, and their limitations in relation to prediction of dangerous behaviour are assessed. Dr Blackburn's consideration of psychometrics and personality theory in relation to dangerous offending is of current relevance, since personality tests are widely used in a number of large security hospitals. The question of reliability and validity of the measurement of such personality traits as 'psychopathy' are of considerable importance to psychologists who are asked to provide such assessments for psychiatrists.

In view of the current problems in assessment outlined by Blackburn, it could be suggested that mental health professionals should focus their attention on limited treatment goals, with reference to situations which trigger the specific undesirable behaviours, while bearing in mind generalised personality tendencies. One important area in which psychologists have been particularly successful in regard to this is in the treatment of abnormal sexual offenders. This topic is dealt with by Dr Derek Perkins, a Principal Psychologist in the prison service who has the advantage of being involved in carrying out treatment and conducting therapeutic research and assessment on abnormal sexual offenders in prison. His chapter provides concrete examples of actual assessments and treatments applied to dangerous sexual offenders, and he discusses the problems in predicting future sexual offending. He considers the different nature of various types of sexual offence and reviews important distinctions between the motivations of sexual offenders. The problems of assessment specifically encountered in detention situations (faking, denial, and so on) are clearly outlined. Also he reviews critically the effects of chemical and castration treatments. The whole range of methods and problems encountered in designing, carrying out and evaluating psychological treatment programmes for abnormal sexual offenders is discussed. The successful treatment of the individual who has a persistent predictable pattern of offending and who genuinely wishes to change, is contrasted with the offender who resists examination and who has a record of unpredictable abnormal and violent sexual behaviour. Problems relating to the release of the latter are considered in relation to the concept of 'dangerousness'. Dr Perkins advocates a multidimensional approach to the treatment of sex offenders – tackling social and direct sexual problems. The fact that sex offenders tend to be more anxious and rather less aggressive in general, as Dr Blackburn illustrates in his chapter, may bode well for the co-operation of patients in treatments. There are many important ethical issues raised by Dr Perkins and he expresses concern about a number of medical treatments. It might be considered unfortunate that some of the most successful psychological methods of treatment would provoke public outcry if applied to patients in maximum security hospitals. One of the major questions here is how can successful treatment 'inside' generalise to 'outside'?

Some of the major difficulties and limitations of assessing 'dangerousness' by observations within an institution are reviewed by the present writer. Relevant factors, such as the attitudes of assessors and the nature and stage of incarceration at the time of behaviour observation, are discussed on the basis of the author's research experience in the maximum security hospital setting. Some disconcerting evidence is provided concerning the possible effects of incarceration and/or 'treatment' on the development of behavioural abnormalities. The limitations in generalising from ratings of intra-institutional behaviour to post-release behaviour are emphasised.

The third part of the book presents some recent biochemical and psychological research on some of the characteristics of offenders committed to a maximum security hospital for offences of extreme violence.

Dr Woodman describes the main results of a three-year biochemical study on security hospital patients. His research is linked to a study of psychophysiological differences between security hospital patients (Hinton 1980, 1981). Dr Woodman points to significant differences in hormone balance between offenders committed for 'murderous' offences and those who are not. Such outcomes were predicted from earlier research relating hormone response patterns to anger and fear. The results could have potential implications for differential drug treatments, which might adjust hormone balance and possibly change the propensity for angry violent behaviour under stress anticipation conditions. While such research as Dr Woodman's could lead to systematic psychopharmacological research designed to alleviate the suffering caused by extreme outbursts of angry behaviour, this type of study frequently provokes controversy, as it can be claimed to lead to methods which, if applied unethically, would threaten the civil liberties of those in custody.

On the other hand, while some people may fear possibilities of 'insidious biological manipulation' and have a genuine concern for what could happen to the deviant members of society, it must be borne in mind that the 'drug and shock' methods currently in use are for the most part blunt and dangerous instruments. In my view, the real moral issue is whether it is more ethical to make decisions on treatment and discharge based on very dubious data and subjective opinion as at present, or whether it would be better to have objective data and to know more about what we are doing? The fundamental question is: should scientific advances in our understanding of the link between brain and behaviour be thwarted by our fears of potential practitioners?

One question concerning Dr Woodman's work is which comes first – the physiological condition or the behaviour concerned? In fact one difficulty in this area of research is that studies are inevitably retrospective and so biological states could be the result of the person's reaction to what he did and the way he has been treated as a result. Such studies as Dr Woodman's do, however, provide substantial hypotheses for both prospective and experimental studies of aggressive behaviour.

Dr Howells's chapter is concerned with the assessment and understanding of the subjective cognitive states of violent offenders. He presents and discusses the results of a three-year study on the beliefs and attitudes towards others of individual 'dangerous' offenders detained in a security hospital. The method he employs does allow for statistical comparison between different groups of offender. Using a repertory grid technique, he assesses social evaluations made by different offender types, including the 'one-off' offender – the domestic murderer who is otherwise conforming and peaceable. These offenders appear to have an abnormally unstable system of evaluating people which Dr Howells relates to a personality theory of 'overcontrol'. It is of particular interest that Dr Howells, using a completely different approach to the more conventional psychometric one of Dr Blackburn, comes to the same conclusion that 'overcontrolled' individuals predominate among the 'one-off' murderers found in security hospital.

The final chapters of the book deal with the prospects for improvement in the statistical prediction of dangerous re-offending and the potential of a multidisciplinary approach.

Professor John Copas is a pioneer in the development and application of a new type of prediction equation which overcomes the limitations of the standard statistical techniques hitherto employed in criminology. Specifically, Professor Copas's novel approach is aimed at minimising 'overprediction' – the main problem of current procedures. He cites a recent study, in the prediction of delinquent behaviour, which demonstrates the effectiveness of his technique. This involves the non-linear combination of variables for prediction purposes. A lucid discussion is provided on the factors which have to be considered in applying his method to the prediction of seriously violent re-offending.

The last chapter, by the present writer, argues the case for multidisciplinary teamwork in further research on the understanding and prediction of seriously violent and abnormal offending. A biosocial outlook is proposed in the broadening of the data base. This approach would depend on current empirical research findings and theory which relate extreme physical aggression and recidivism to psychophysiological and biochemical functioning. The biological make-up may be affected by environmental influences which produce a permanent predisposition to react – for instance, without fear or concern for consequence. A proposal is made for the integration of behavioural psychology, neurology, sociology, psychophysiology, biochemistry and psychopharmacology in the study of dangerousness. An outline is provided of some of the factors which are restricting research, and in this regard a number of contentious points are made based on the author's five-year experience with a research unit attached to a maximum security hospital.

Recent advances in research and computer techniques allow the rapid and accurate collection and analysis of data over many of the areas discussed in this book. With a broad spread of data, and using new developments in non-linear probabilistic prediction, as explained by Professor Copas, it may eventually be possible to provide the decision-makers with at least a little of the objective information they require. Thus, if indeterminate detention is to be retained, some of the ethical objections due to subjectivity and high uncertainty in decision-making could, perhaps, be alleviated.

Part One

Ethical, Political and Professional Problems and Controversies on their Resolution

2 Dangerousness and Rights

ANTHONY E. BOTTOMS AND
ROGER BROWNSWORD

In recent years, in Britain, we have seen proposals for the creation of special sentences for the dangerous offender from the Scottish Council on Crime (1975), the Butler Committee (1975) and, in a rather different form, from the Advisory Council on the Penal System (1978). One of us has contributed to the general debate surrounding these proposals, casting doubts on their soundness (Bottoms, 1977, 1981). It is not proposed to go over this ground again here.

A recent Home Office Research Unit report refers to Bottoms's 1977 paper and states that he and other authors seem to 'assume that the dangerous offender exists as no more than a symbol of bourgeois fears or of bureaucratic repression' (Brody and Tarling, 1980, p. 33). At least so far as the reference to Bottoms is concerned, we can say with some certainty that this is a wholly erroneous inference. Nevertheless, the error may have an importance of its own in pointing to a neglected feature of the dangerousness debate, namely, the possible conflict between utility and rights.

Those who oppose the creation of fresh sentences for the dangerous offender (whom we may call 'libertarians'), generally do so knowing full well that the absence of such sentences will lead to a slightly higher violent crime rate in the community. At the same time these libertarians wish to stress the importance of, as they see it, the individual rights of the persons liable to be subjected to preventive custody, and to set these in the scales against the reduction of assaults in considering the overall penal policy. By contrast, at least some of those who advocate special protective measures against the dangerous (whom we may call 'protectionists') tend to have a much more sceptical view of offenders' rights, or at any rate their natural rights, which is what is in issue here (for example, Walker, 1980, ch. 8). If such a view is taken, clearly there is little or nothing to set in the policy scales against the expected slight reduction in assaults arising from the dangerousness sentence, and so the sentence is favoured. Those who are explicitly or implicitly sceptical about rights may well fail to realise the importance that libertarians attach to this concept: hence they may falsely assume (as Brody and Tarling do, whether or not for this reason) that for the libertarian the dangerous offender as such does not exist at all.

In this paper we wish to clarify and state more fully than hitherto a libertarian case on dangerousness, based on a concept of rights. We shall do so by considering the utilitarian view and two versions of possible rights theories.

It is our concern here to concentrate on the ethical issues rather than the empirical research on dangerousness. Hence for the purposes of this argument we will assume a basic agreement on the relevant arithmetic as between the protectionist and the libertarian. Nigel Walker (1978, p. 41), in his protectionist article, has put the matter like this:

> we have not yet succeeded in providing criteria which would ensure that a prediction of future violence would be right more often than it would be wrong. With present criteria, it would more often be wrong . . . it will mean detaining two or three (or even more) individuals in order to prevent only one of them from committing further violence.

Bottoms (1977, p. 80), in his libertarian article, similarly argued that 'at the present time, the best we can do is to produce a false positive rate of between 55 and 70 per cent' (see further Bottoms, 1981). Thus for the purposes of this paper we will assume, rather crudely, a broad consensus around the two-to-one figure: that is, that for every three offenders one locks up as potentially dangerous, only one would in actuality have turned out to be so.

Accepting this figure as a baseline, the essential policy issue then is, how far is it justifiable to lock people up, in the name of public protection, for longer than their offence warrants on the normal deterrent and retributive criteria? And in order to highlight the ethical issues involved here, it is instructive to take an imaginary example: suppose there were three innocent and mentally normal people who have not yet committed any known crime, would we be justified in locking them all up because we believed on good grounds that one of them was in the future likely to commit serious violence?

We think there would be an almost unanimous judgement against taking such powers. Clearly, however, many people would make a very different judgement with three people who have been convicted: with the latter they would have no qualms about locking them up for longer than the normal term because of the evidence of a one in three chance of future serious violence. But can the two examples be rationally differentiated? We shall look at this key question in the light of our three chosen ethical positions, namely, utilitarianism and two versions of rights theory.

Utilitarianism

In its original and most straightforward form, utilitarianism is an ethical position which can be expressed as a combination of two principles: the *consequentialist principle* that the rightness or wrongness of an action is determined by the goodness or badness of the results that flow from it, and the *hedonist principle* that the only thing that is good in itself is pleasure, and the only thing bad in itself is pain. Hence utilitarians believe that *the rightness of an action is ultimately determined by its contribution to the happiness of everyone affected by it* (Quinton, 1973, p. 1).

It is easy to see how utilitarians defend protective sentences for the dangerous convicted offender. The happiness of those likely to be seriously assaulted will be much greater if they are not actually subjected to assault. The happiness of the great majority of right-thinking members of society will be a little increased if they can know that the serious crime rate has been slightly reduced, and their own psychological security a little increased, at marginal cost in terms of income tax. Set against all this is the pain of those who are subjected to continuing detention; but as to this, it can be seen as quantitatively less than the pleasure of the potential victims and the rest of society put together, whilst qualitatively 'the death or injury of a blameless victim cannot be put in the same moral scales as the further detention of a person who has culpably done, risked, attempted or threatened serious harm' (Advisory Council on the Penal System, 1978, p. 90).

It is also possible on utilitarian principles to defend *not* locking up three innocent and mentally normal citizens to prevent one serious assault. The happiness of those likely to be assaulted would, of course, be the same if protective sentences were introduced for this group as for the earlier case. But one could argue (*a*) that the pain to those who are locked up is much greater in this case, since they are innocent citizens who have been picked up off the streets and subjected to long detention; and (*b*) that the members of society generally would be disturbed by the principle of locking up the innocent, and perhaps marginally anxious about their own freedom, so that their happiness at the slight reduction of the crime rate would be at least cancelled out by this increased pain. Thus, in sum, the pleasure–pain calculus might well come out on the side of pain in this case, in contrast to the earlier case: hence, measures of this kind should not be introduced.

Whilst this position may seem satisfactory to protectionists, it contains one fatal flaw. This is, simply, that the straightforward utilitarian position produces no safeguard to the innocent against imprisonment on the grounds of social utility in cases where the pleasure–pain calculus *does* produce an advantage in favour of detention. And, as many ethical writers have pointed out, it is certainly quite possible to conceive of situations where the locking up of an innocent scapegoat would be for the overall advantage of society in strictly utilitarian terms. Thus, unless we wish to endorse this practice, we cannot ultimately be satisfied with a simple utilitarian approach.[1]

Rawls (1972, p. 3) has neatly characterised the objection to this kind of utilitarianism in his famous opening passage:

Justice is the first virtue of social institutions, as truth is of systems of thought. A theory however elegant and economical must be rejected or revised if it is untrue; likewise laws and institutions no matter how efficient and well-arranged must be reformed or abolished if they are unjust. Each person possesses an inviolability founded on justice that even the welfare of society as a whole cannot override.

In other words, for Rawls, even if one accepts the general welfare as a guiding principle for social or penal policy, there are points at which that general welfare must give way to the justice owed to the individual (as, in the instant case, to the innocent scapegoat who is selected for punishment). We cannot enter here into the considerable complexities of the theory of justice that Rawls espouses, but it is quite clear that in his detailed scheme individuals can be said to have *rights* which sometimes override general social utility. Acting on this insight, it may be possible to construct a penal policy which *in general* seeks to maximise society's welfare and happiness, but allows that principle to be overridden *at certain points* by the rights of individuals. In using the word 'rights' here we deliberately do so in the same strong sense as Dworkin (1978, p. 256):

> The only clear and useful definition of what a right is uses this opposition between rights and the general welfare. Someone has a right, in this strong and useful sense, when he is entitled to insist on doing something or having something even though the general welfare is harmed thereby.

If, because of the innocent scapegoat problem, we are convinced that simple utilitarianism cannot solve our penal policy dilemmas, can we adopt a version of rights theory instead? And, if we do, what are the consequences for the dangerous offender problem?

Rights Theory I

We shall derive the first version of rights theory which we consider largely from the work of H. L. A. Hart. We have to say in advance that we cannot be sure that Hart himself would approve the conclusions we have drawn from his general approach. But we are clear that the position advanced is an interesting and important one, whether or not Hart would himself endorse it.

Hart (1968) at various points distinguishes between the general justifying aim of punishment (that is, its main purpose as a social institution), and the *allocation* or *distribution* of punishment to individuals, both in terms of liability (who may be punished?) and amount (to what extent?). He clearly shows that it is rationally possible to be a utilitarian in general justifying theory, while adopting a different principle for questions of liability or amount. In this way he distinguishes his position from that of the simple utilitarian (see pp. 75–82).

Particular attention is paid to the issue of *liability*, and within that to the questions of strict liability and of punishing the innocent. Both are rejected, and punishment is, in general, restricted in Hart's scheme to those who have broken the law, and also to those who have done so with *mens rea*. This is because 'out of considerations of fairness or justice to individuals we should restrict even punishment designed as a "preventive" to those who had a normal capacity and a fair opportunity to obey' (p. 201).

In elaborating this principle, particular emphasis is placed on the importance of *choice* for the individual:

First, the individual has an option between obeying or paying. The worse the laws are, the more valuable the possibility of exercising this choice becomes in enabling an individual to decide how he shall live. Secondly, this system not only enables individuals to exercise this choice but increases the power of individuals to identify beforehand periods when the law's punishments will not interfere with them and to plan their lives accordingly. (p.23)

Thus, what we have here is the following. The general object of a penal system is to reduce crimes. But this does not mean that this is an absolute priority: when we decide who to punish we should in general punish only those who have *knowingly broken the law*. We make this restriction out of considerations of fairness or justice to individuals, and in that regard we respect their rights, even at the price of some social utility. In respecting these rights, we stress especially the principle of choice: the position essentially depends on the view that people have a *right to freedom*, which entails that they should not be interfered with unless they have deliberately chosen to risk forfeiting that freedom by knowingly breaking the law.[2]

Now a principle of this kind (which may be termed 'retribution in distribution')[3] would clearly protect innocent people against preventive sentences for dangerousness; and it would do so in the name of a principle of justice, or rights, which is secure against difficulties of the innocent scapegoat in a way that simple utilitarianism is not. It seems therefore to be a superior principle.

But what would this principle achieve in relation to possible preventive sentences for those already convicted? We may look at this in two ways: first in terms of general principle, and secondly in terms of what Hart has to say about limiting the *amount* of punishment.

In terms of general principle, a view which stresses choice seems to offer little to individual offenders seeking to avoid the application of a preventive sentence. Suppose the law says that for a given offence, the normal penalty is x, but that in addition those convicted of the offence are liable to be screened for preventive detention on the grounds of their dangerousness, and if labelled as dangerous may be kept beyond the normal limit of x years. Even though only one in three of those labelled as dangerous actually will be so, all those who broke the law knew (or could have known) at the time of breaking it that they were rendering themselves liable for a preventive sentence. Thus, on the principle of choice, they have no complaint if they are locked up as dangerous.

Exegesis of Hart produces much the same result, though on different grounds. A limiting principle on the amount of punishment can be either *absolute* (punishment must not exceed a fixed amount) or *relative* (punishment as between comparable offenders must not be disproportionate). An absolute limiting principle can be based either on retribution or utility (p. 234). If the former, it sets upper limits on punishments proportionate to the moral gravity of the offence; if the latter, the relevant principles are forward-looking rather than backward-looking – minor harms are not to be punished with a severity which creates greater misery than the offence would if left unchecked, and so forth. Of these principles, only the retributively based principle (known as 'limiting retribution') can generate rights, in our sense; utility theories cannot by definition generate rights in the strong sense. And it is clear that Hart prefers the utilitarian approach when limiting amount of punishment (pp. 162–3).

As regards the relative principle, or the notion of respect for a principle of equality and fairness as between different offenders, Hart is prepared to accord this a 'modest place' in his penal philosophy,

> but not as something which warrants going beyond the requirements of the forward-looking aims of deterrence, prevention and reform to find some apt expression of moral feeling. Fairness between different offenders expressed in terms of different punishments is not an end in itself . . . we should give effect to it where it does not impede the pursuit of the main aims of punishment. (p. 172)

A modest and secondary principle of this kind clearly cannot generate any rights for the offender reaching the end of his normal term and potentially subject to preventive custody as dangerous.

Thus general principle and exegesis of Hart both produce the same result. We can under this second theory justify not applying a preventive sentence to the three innocents, on the basis of a principle of freedom of choice, while at the same time the utilitarian general justifying aim permits us to apply the preventive sentence to the three offenders, without hindrance from any right which can limit the amount of punishment.

However, there are three possible objections to this general position. First, in the strong sense of 'right' which we are using, the only right generated by this approach is the right not to be interfered with unless one has knowingly broken the law. Provided that a dangerousness sentence is specified by the law, it can on this view be legitimately attached to *any* offence, however trivial; for the offender would or could still know before committing the offence that it might render him liable for the special sentence. But this may seem to draw too sharp a distinction between the non-offender and the offender. If it is right not to lock up the non-offender as dangerous, is it really just and fair to lock up indefinitely, on the basis of a one in three prediction, one who is charged with breach of the peace after thoughtlessly becoming involved in a pub brawl?

If the first obection considers one aspect of the theory too harsh, the second wonders whether it is too libertarian. For this version of rights theory seems on the face of it to produce an absolute protection against detaining the innocent. But what if temporary detention of a few days could be shown certainly to save thousands of lives? Is the prohibition on detention really absolute?

Hart himself concedes that if pressed he would make exceptions. 'Given enough misery to be avoided by the sacrifice of an innocent person, there may be situations in which it might be thought morally permissible to take this step' (p. 81). Sensible though this concession seems, it nevertheless places Hart in some theoretical difficulty. For there is no clear principle on which his exception is made, in relation to the general theory of choice which surrounds it. Rather the exception seems to be born of a pragmatic approach. Yet if we are to make this kind of very rare exception, it surely needs to be on the basis of a grounded principle, not just pragmatic expediency.

Thirdly, this version of rights theory seems vulnerable to attacks springing from the principle of equality. Many legal systems recognise the importance of the general principle that 'like cases must be treated alike', even though they may differ on what constitutes a like case. An offender potentially subject to a preventive sentence for dangerousness is liable to be detained for much longer than his confederate who has committed the same offence but has not been classified as dangerous; and there is a high probability that in terms of actual dangerousness the two do not differ. It is clear therefore that the dangerousness issue does raise moral problems about equality of treatment, although this is not to say that these problems are to be solved by any mechanical application of simple rules. Hart's approach, in which equality is given a firmly secondary place, may not seem to give sufficient weight to the instinct for justice which the equality principle enshrines. There is also, it has to be said, an even more damaging attack springing from equality, an attack which threatens to undermine the whole theoretical basis of this version of rights theory. It has been persuasively argued by Steven Lukes (1973) that the idea of freedom (of which choice is a crucial component) is intimately related to the idea of equal respect for persons, such that the latter idea is centrally involved in giving an account of what it is to be free. If, as Lukes suggests, the key concept here is equality as equal respect, then Hart's freedom-based rights thesis is locked into a structure of ideas which orbit around equal respect; and there is then no way that equality can be held at arm's length. This suggests that a rights theory based on a principle of equality may have more to commend it.

Rights Theory II

The recent and influential rights theory of Ronald Dworkin (1977), which is at core based on the equality principle, seems to us to overcome the difficulties in the first version of rights theory, and to achieve a distinctively different result. Again, however, we have to make the preliminary disclaimer that we cannot be sure Dworkin would endorse all the conclusions which we draw from his work.

Dworkin's approach, being a general theory of rights, is complex. We will seek to present it sequentially, handling *first* his formal theory of the nature of rights (without reference to the content of those rights); *secondly* the content of rights; and *thirdly* the application of these principles to the criminal justice system and to dangerousness sentences.

We have already seen that for Dworkin (1978, p. 256) the concept of rights has a restricted meaning, and is used only where a right may be claimed in opposition to the general welfare. If someone has such a right, then it is wrong for the government to deny it to him even though it would be in the general interest to do so (Dworkin, 1977, p. 269). Hence in this terminology we cannot speak of, for example, having a 'right' to do something just because it is not morally wrong to do it: the claim must be much stronger than that.

Can rights, in this strong sense, ever be overridden? Dworkin's answer is affirmative (Dworkin, 1977, p. 200), and the most important ground for overriding them is that others have 'competing rights that would be jeopardised if the right in question were not limited' (p. 193). In considering competing rights, however, we cannot speak of the competing rights of society at large (or of any large sub-group of society), for this would merely be to reintroduce the forbidden priority of the general welfare. Hence we should restrict ourselves to considering the competing rights of *other individuals* (p. 194).

There is a particularly important contrast here with simple utilitarianism which needs to be brought out more fully. We saw that in constructing the pleasure–pain calculus on dangerousness sentences the utilitarian included within the equation the pleasure or pain of members of society as a whole, who were not directly involved in possible injuries. But in Dworkin's theory, this pleasure or pain is irrelevant once it is established that another individual has a right. Furthermore, Dworkin also wishes, even when utilitarian calculations about the general welfare are being made, to purge utility of any strength it acquires from the 'external preferences' of people not directly involved (pp. 234–6, 275–8, 357–8).

Dworkin does not discuss in detail how the balancing of competing individual rights is to be achieved, but he does enunciate one important general principle. If there are competing rights, then one right cannot *automatically* be overridden or made subordinate to another. For 'if rights make sense, then the degrees of their importance cannot be so different that some count not at all when others are mentioned' (pp. 203–4).

So far we have said nothing at all about the contents of rights, but have merely discussed their formal nature. How do we discover whether a particular right exists?

Dworkin's approach to this is as follows. If rights in the strong sense exist, then asserting them is a serious business, for it 'makes the Government's job of securing the general benefit more difficult and more expensive' (p. 198). We must therefore have serious core principles in mind when asserting rights; and these core principles must be of sufficient importance to justify overriding the general welfare. Two key ideas suggested are those of *human dignity* and *political equality* (p. 198). These are combined by Dworkin to produce the master-principle of *a right to concern and respect which is equal as between citizens* (pp. 272–3). From this central principle, which of course closely resembles that of Lukes (see above), more particular and specific rights may be derived, in a number of ways.

The notion of equality requires elaboration. There are two different ideas which might be encompassed by it: the right to exactly *equal treatment*, or the right to *treatment as an equal*, that is, 'the right not to an equal distribution of some good or opportunity, but the right to equal concern and respect in the political decision about how these goods and opportunities are to be distributed' (p. 273). Dworkin makes it clear that for him the second principle is the more fundamental one.

How might such a theoretical approach be applied to the problems of criminal justice? Dworkin in fact devotes little systematic attention to criminal law, but his book does contain a brief discussion of Hart's theories of punishment (pp. 8–13). He is sceptical of Hart's argument about choice grounding a concept of retribution in distribution. Rather, he argues that such a concept can be more successfully based on the principle that 'the government must treat its citizens with the respect and dignity that adult members of the community claim from each other' (p. 11). Then, if as a society we abrogate the principle of retribution in distribution (as, perhaps, we should in the case of civil commitment statutes for the mentally ill), 'we ought to recognise the compromise with principle that this policy involves; and should treat a man against his will only when the danger he presents is vivid, not whenever we calculate that it would probably reduce crime if we did' (p. 11).

Relating this conclusion to the general theory of rights elaborated earlier proceeds as follows. Citizens have rights against the general welfare if and only if such rights can be derived from the master-principle of equal concern and respect. That principle of concern and respect requires the government to take account of intentions and motivations in criminal law, as well as not to punish the innocent; thus it gives innocent persons and inadvertent perpetrators of criminal acts a general right not to be punished. That right cannot be overridden by considerations of the general welfare, nor by the opinions of the mass of society, however strong they may be. However, the right can (as in the case of the mentally abnormal civil commitment case) be set directly against the competing rights of potential victims not to be assaulted, for these citizens are entitled to insist on their right to go about their business without attack, even if for some reason such peaceful progression were considered contrary to the general welfare. In weighing these competing rights of the potential victim and the innocent person potentially subject to civil commitment, both must be treated seriously. Dworkin's own suggestion is that we should not detain the man unless 'the danger he presents is vivid'.

The concept of vivid danger needs more analysis than Dworkin gives it. We suggest that it has three main components: *seriousness* (what type and degree of injury is in contemplation?); *temporality*, which breaks down into *frequency* (over a given period, how many injurious acts are expected?) and *immediacy* (how soon is the next injurious act?); and, *certainty* (how sure are we that this person will act as predicted?). The certainty element is pivotal. If there is a very low score on the certainty factor, then whatever the danger it is hardly vivid. However, as the score increases on the certainty element, the risk becomes increasingly vivid and we then have to look very carefully at the kind of danger threatened. Clearly, a low score on the seriousness scale is going to militate strongly against the danger being described as vivid.

Returning to the civil commitment case, we agree with Dworkin that the 'vivid danger' test is a fair one. If we are going to lock up a man against his will we are *certainly* acting against his right; but there is often no certainty that a crime will result from his being left at large, or, if it will, that it will be serious or happen soon. The man is therefore entitled to insist that his right not to be detained should not be overridden unless, on an amalgam of these factors, the rights of others really are substantially threatened – in other words, that the danger he presents is vivid.

Consider now the problem of whether to lock up the three mentally normal innocents to save one violent crime. The three have the right not to be locked up, such right being defensible only where the exercise of the right presents a vivid danger to competing rights. Might the vivid danger test be satisfied? Given that the probability of violence is only one in three, there is a low score on certainty. Not only that, the record of the three innocents is necessarily going to discourage high scores on seriousness and temporality. Thus, it is barely conceivable that the vivid danger test would ever be met.[4] In which case Dworkin, albeit for a different reason, would arrive at the same general conclusion as Hart on this point.

When we turn to the three convicted offenders facing a dangerousness sentence, the first question is to establish whether or not they have a right (in the sense in which we are using the word) to be released at the end of their normal sentence.

We think they do, and we could argue for this right in either of two ways. First, we might follow Dworkin's strategy (ch. 12) in allocating rights to individuals in just those situations where, drawing on our general knowledge of society, we anticipate that the decision will 'have been reached by virtue of the external components of the preferences democracy reveals' (p. 277). In other words, where a political decision seems antecedently likely to contain external preferences, then individuals are insulated through a distribution of rights; this is done in response to the practical impossibility of eliminating external preferences from decisions made in a democratic society. Thus, if – as we suppose – decisions on dangerousness sentences might be expected to draw on external preferences, those potentially affected should have the protection of rights. In this way the dangerous offender would be put beyond the reach of a decision that might treat him with less than equal concern and respect.

If this first line of argument seems unnecessarily tortuous, there remains a second strategy which is far more direct. This second argument for the dangerous offender's rights runs in this form. During his prison term the prisoner is not treated on the same basis as an ordinary citizen. There are chronic disabilities: loss of liberty, restricted communication with outsiders, and so on. Whatever justification there is for such treatment, it terminates at the end of the normal term of imprisonment. At the end of the normal term the offender is entitled to be viewed as a full member of the human community, that is, to be treated again as an ordinary citizen. It is therefore surely beyond dispute that the right to equal concern and respect generates directly in the dangerous offender the right to release at normal term. For, if he is denied this right the dangerous offender is treated as less than a full citizen.[5]

Given that the offender has a right to release at normal term the justification for blocking that right through a dangerousness sentence must proceed on exactly the same basis as it would in the case of an innocent subject. Therefore, we must implement the right to release unless the offender presents a vivid danger to the competing rights of others. In applying one and the same criterion to both offenders and innocents, this third theory differs dramatically from the second theory which we considered.

We said earlier, when discussing the three innocent persons, that with a one in three certainty base it was scarcely credible that the vivid danger test could be satisfied. Since the certainty base remains constant when we turn to offenders, does it follow that here too it is virtually inconceivable that the vivid danger test would be met?

Consider the following case. A man was sent to Broadmoor for an offence of poisoning; he was eventually conditionally released from that Special Hospital, but within nine months of release had committed two murders, two attempted murders and two offences of causing grievous bodily harm, all by poisoning, and all on different victims (Holden, 1974). In principle, would we now accept a dangerousness sentence in this case?

The answer to this turns on the seriousness and temporality components of the vivid danger test. In this case under consideration we have high ratings on both these elements. On the basis of the past brutal behaviour we might expect future very serious injury, multiple injury, and all very rapidly. If our assessment is correct and this man presents these risks to the rights of others then he really is dangerous. But, of course, there is a two to one chance that we are wrong in our assessment. Even so, it is eminently arguable that we do have here enough to overcome the vivid danger test, and so to keep him beyond normal term.

The feature of the case just considered which is crucial in tipping the balance is the past behaviour of the offender. Even in conditions of low certainty there comes a point where vivid danger is arguable by virtue of high scores on seriousness and temporality. But it is only where there is a record of serious violence that we can expect to return such high ratings. Thus, while there is no difference whatsoever in the status of offenders and innocents as right-holders, nevertheless at the evidential level the offender's record can be a distinguishing factor when the vivid danger test is applied.

Although we are allowing the possibility of the vivid danger test going against an offender with a serious record of violence, we are conceiving of this as a quite exceptional case. Our position is therefore markedly different from that of most protectionists. As an example we might consider the new 'exceptional sentence' proposed by the Advisory Council on the Penal System (1978): this would be a term of fixed duration, but with no maximum limit, for, in effect, those considered as dangerous. At least two features of the Council's approach are worrying. First, the Council's conception of the 'serious harm' to be prevented by the exceptional sentence is very broad, running from serious personal injury through exceptional financial loss to damage to the general fabric of society. The crucial question is not whether this conception of serious harm fits with our ordinary understanding, but whether even if harm of some of the kinds specified were *certain* to occur, they would override the offender's right to be released at normal term.[6] And this we doubt. Secondly, as we have previously noted, the Council holds that injury to 'a blameless victim cannot be put in the same moral scales as the further detention of a person who has culpably done, risked, attempted or threatened serious harm'

(p. 90). In so far as this implies that the dangerous offender has no rights, or that his rights should be weighed perfunctorily, we disagree. But if our position differs from that struck by the Advisory Council, it differs also – although less radically – from the line taken by Radzinowicz and Hood (1978) in their critical review of the Council's report. They conclude that the concept of dangerousness 'is so insidious that it should never be introduced in penal legislation, let alone under such a broad canopy' (p. 722). We do not say that a dangerousness sentence could never be justified. Our view is that in the present state of the evidence it would take a remarkable case to justify a dangerousness sentence on an offender, and in the case of a mentally normal non-offender we find it almost impossible to conceive of a justified detention.

Even though we do not go all the way with Radzinowicz and Hood, we share their anxiety that the Council's definition of dangerousness is such as 'would be received with open arms by any authoritarian state', and their concern at the 'potentialities for accelerating use and shameful abuse' inherent in the concept of dangerousness (p. 719). Indeed, even if our 'vivid danger' test were being applied, we have anxieties about the actual execution of the test. Presumably it would be applied either by a court or by the equivalent of a parole board. Can we be sure that the members of such a body would balance right against competing right with complete impartiality, and that they would not be swayed (as, under Dworkin's approach, they should not be swayed) by the 'external preferences' of ministers or of public opinion?

Merely to ask this question is to recognise the impossible pressures upon the decision-makers. It leads us to a further stage which is a slight extension of Dworkin's theory. We have seen that Dworkin wishes to give individuals rights in precisely those situations where external preferences seem antecedently likely to contaminate political decisions: it is an insurance to those potentially affected, in pursuit of the principle that the state should not lose sight of their claim to equal concern and respect.

But there are certain situations, of which the problem considered in this paper is an example, where any right given will almost automatically compete with another right. It is then important that both rights shall be given their full weighting; but it is also of crucial importance to ensure that when competing rights are being weighed in a discretionary decision-making situation, issues of general utility and external preferences do not enter the discussion. If this seems likely to happen – as it does in the dangerousness case – then rules must be built in to prevent it.

We suggest that, in the present state of knowledge, this should be done by limiting the possibility of the protective sentence to those who have already caused or attempted very serious violence. We recognise that this is a somewhat crude move, and that it may seem strange to shift from 'future vivid danger' to 'past very serious harm'. But, as quoted by Walker in Chapter 3 of this book, 'nothing predicts behaviour like behaviour': since the subject has a right to be released at normal term unless 'vivid danger' can be adduced against him, to guard against external preferences it is fair to restrict the dangerousness sentence, in the present frail state of scientific prediction, to those who have already caused vivid danger in their past record. In our judgement the principle of equal concern and respect demands nothing less.

It could be objected that by restricting protective detention for offenders to those with past very serious violence, we have deviated from the principle of using the same criterion for innocents and offenders alike. But we would deny this. Both groups are to be regulated under the master-principle of equal concern and respect, and it is this principle which requires extra protection for the offender to guard against external preferences. Such guarding is not needed for the innocent, against whom public opinion is not prejudiced. Equal concern and respect does not necessarily mean exactly equal treatment.

The result we have arrived at is broadly congruent with the earlier conclusion of Bottoms (1977), reached on a less closely reasoned basis, that on present evidence dangerousness sentences should not be passed 'except on one who has already committed an act of really extreme severity, such as murder or attempted murder' (pp. 80–1). The set of principles we have argued for would also, of course, lead to a much more restrictive use of preventive sentences for the dangerous than is proposed in the reports of the Butler Committee, the Scottish Council on Crime, and the Advisory Council on the Penal System.

Conclusion

We have argued for an approach to dangerousness sentences based on Dworkin's theory of rights. Throughout, we have operated on the assumption that on present evidence the best we can achieve is a false positive rate of about 60 per cent. But it is important to notice that, if the empirical contingencies change, the general principles of the approach would still hold. 'Vivid danger' would remain the ultimate test, and the components of certainty, seriousness and temporality would all need careful examination in changed empirical conditions.

The most important way in which our principles differ from the usual approach of protectionists is in yielding a *prima facie* right to release for the prisoner at the end of his normal term. Walker (Chapter 3), criticising those who hold such a view, argues that 'it seeks to impose restrictions on the law enforcement system which we do not impose on other social institutions', and gives some examples: 'One is the disqualification of epileptics from driving. Another is the restrictions which we place on people who are known or suspected to carry diseases with a high mortality rate, such as smallpox, typhoid, lassa fever, or Marburg virus.'

In so far as Walker is objecting to a view which says that in principle we should *never*, in the penal system, take power over people's lives on the basis of predictions of their future dangerousness, his argument is correct. But that is not the principle that our approach yields. And the examples which he gives are capable of analysis by the third theory in terms of the principles of rights and competing rights, in exactly the same way as other puzzling social problems: in such an analysis the high certainty and extreme seriousness and immediacy of the danger presented by the high mortality diseases would be an important factor, as would scepticism about whether one has a *right* to drive, assertable against the general welfare, in quite the same way that one has a right not to be locked up. Therefore Walker's argument, in the next chapter, in no sense invalidates the general approach we have advocated here.

Notes: Chapter 2

1   There are, of course, revised versions of utilitarianism which might offer a better prospect of fielding this objection, for example, rule-utilitarianism or utility with a caveat for gross inequality of distress (cf. Honderich, 1976). We have no space to treat these theories here, though we consider that neither adequately handles the problem while remaining utilitarian. Rule-utilitarianism keeps its ultimately empirical criterion of utility and is vulnerable where (i) there is a rule protecting the innocent from detention but in a given case the utilities would clearly favour protective action, or (ii) the utilities themselves alter so that locking up the innocent would produce greater overall utility than a rule not to do so. The Honderich line uses equality as a stopping principle and therefore in our view ultimately turns into a version of rights theory.

2   Elsewhere, Hart (1955) argued a general case that 'if there are any moral rights at all, it follows that there is at least one natural right, the equal right of all men to be free'. However, the relationship between this claim and Hart's later work on punishment is not straightforward, and cannot be pursued here.

3   So called because it limits liability by reference to a past act which is deserving of punishment. This should not be confused with retribution as the general justifying aim of punishment; nor with retribution as a limiting principle to limit the *amount* of punishment by reference to the moral gravity of the past act ('limiting retribution').

4   In a truly exceptional case it is just conceivable. Even then, Dworkin's theory differs from utilitarianism, which puts at risk the innocent scapegoat: for Dworkin, the scapegoat's exercise of his rights presents no danger to the rights of others, so he could never be locked up.

5   Since this argument holds, it becomes unnecessary for us to argue whether Dworkin's general approach also yields an absolute limitation on the amount of punishment, specified by reference to the moral gravity of the offence ('limiting retribution'). This is a complex argument, but we think that the approach will yield such a principle.

6   The Council recommended lower normal terms; this does not affect our argument, since the offender has the right to release at normal term, whatever it is.

3 Protecting People

NIGEL D. WALKER

If – as so often happens – someone opens his discussion of a concept by reciting a dictionary's definition, this suggests to me that he himself is unsure what he is talking about. In any case, if the concept is sufficiently controversial to merit discussion, the dictionary is probably misleading. Dictionaries are after all compiled by people in back rooms, consulting publications rather than listening to contemporary conversations. Even when they look at the printed word they seldom think of legal usage.

In the case of 'dangerousness' this is especially striking. One author, for example, begins an otherwise excellent article with the Oxford Dictionary's definition of 'danger' as 'power of a lord or master' (dominium): a usage which is so archaic – to use that Dictionary's own term – that it has ceased to have any relevance to the modern meaning. Equally out of date and irrelevant are such meanings as '1. Liability (to loss) . . . 2. Difficulty . . . chariness, coyness. . . .'. Etymological history is bunk.

Even '3. Mischief or harm' is out of date. In modern usage, a danger is not an actual mischief or harm, but one which is possible or likely. A dangerous situation, action, or activity is one which makes some kind of harm more likely than usual.

Nor are we thinking of any kind of harm when we use the word 'danger'. We usually have in mind serious and not trivial harm. Betting a small sum of money on an 'outsider' is merely 'risky': it is risking all or most of one's capital that would be 'dangerous'. Climbing over a barbed wire fence is not dangerous: driving across a railway line in front of an approaching train is.

The likelihood of harm, however, must be more than negligible. Investing all one's money in government loan stock is not dangerous: nor is driving across a railway line when the signal indicates that this is safe. Our whole lives are surrounded by innumerable but negligible possibilities of dreadful harm; but we do not regard ourselves as living dangerously. A dangerous situation, action, or activity is one which raises the probability of serious harm above a certain level.

To define that level is not easy, but perhaps not impossible. It is the level which causes a person who is not neurotically or superstitiously anxious to become so apprehensive that he explores the possibility of avoiding the situation, action, or activity. Obviously this level varies with the nature of the apprehended harm. The threshold is lower for rabies than for jaundice: higher for a broken neck than a broken leg.

It is tempting to say, pseudo-scientifically, that *danger* = *seriousness* x *probability of harm*. This ignores one fact, however: that if either seriousness or probability is below a certain level we do not think of the situation as dangerous. It also assumes that the relationship is multiplicative, whereas we do not know this. Research might conceivably show that a more complex mathematical expression would fit our way of thinking about danger: but surely it would merely lend precision to what is already sufficiently obvious.

Dangerousness and Penology

In penology the concept of dangerousness presents legislators with two problems. One is the selection of activities for inclusion in the criminal law; the other is the selection of people for special measures of control. The state of play, however, is quite different in each case. It is universally accepted that certain activities should be made criminal because of the grave harms which they may cause. Examples are the importation without quarantine of animals which may be carrying rabies or other fatal diseases; or the manufacture of toxic substances without precautions against the exposure of the public to them. Such disagreement as exists is concerned mainly with the list of such activities and the machinery of control. This is not to overlook the question of the extent to which decisions may be biased by commercial, political, or ideological interests. The point for the moment, however, is that nobody denies the necessity for legislative control of a large number of activities because of their 'dangerousness'.

Dangerous People?

On the other hand, a lot of people question the ethics of labelling a specified individual as dangerous in order to justify special measures of control. Their arguments vary. Some hold that labelling a man as dangerous can make him more so, or even make a dangerous man out of a non-dangerous one: see for example Sarbin, 1967. The way in which he is treated by police and prison staff can make him respond aggressively to any attempts to control him, or indeed to other forms of frustration when he is at liberty again. This is not, however, an argument against labelling anyone as dangerous, but against careless labelling and certain techniques of inmate-management.

More to the point is the argument that dangerousness should never be ascribed to people, only to situations, actions, or activities. It is this argument that has to be taken seriously, if only because it is taken seriously.

It is a very sweeping argument, and contrary to normal usage. We not only call things like unexploded bombs or rickety bridges 'dangerous': we apply the term to some animals and some people. If pressed we can usually say what the danger is: that a horse may kick or bolt, for example, or that a man may do violence or commit a very harmful indiscretion.

What is said to be wrong with this usage is that it 'objectifies' the danger, by talking as if it were a characteristic of the person, instead of something that he might do in certain circumstances. If so, there must be the same objection to calling people 'loyal', 'truthful', 'irritable', or 'deceitful'. We do not mean that they are always behaving loyally, truthfully, irritably, or deceitfully: only that this is how they usually behave in circumstances which test those qualities.

Nor do we mean, as objectors sometimes assume, that a man who is labelled as dangerously violent will inevitably injure someone who annoys or frustrates him. Not only do we make allowances for circumstances – such as the presence or absence of a policeman – but we also recognise the fact that a man's self-control varies, so that one day he will react violently to an insult which on another day he might swallow. All that we mean is that he is more likely than most people we know – or know of – to react violently.

Sometimes of course – but fortunately not often – we are talking about people who do not merely do harm as a reaction to a situation, but about people who seek out opportunities for harm. Some men go out looking for a fight: a few sexual offenders actively seek out victims. There are opportunity-takers and opportunity-makers as well as reactors.

The Ethical Issue

If on the other hand the real objection is not to linguistic usage but to policies based on labelling people as dangerous, this deserves a much more serious discussion. What gives rise to understandable misgivings in penology and psychiatry is the fact – and it *is* a fact – that in the name of public protection psychiatrists, sentencers, parole authorities, are detaining people against their will *for longer periods than they can justify on other grounds.* Let us accept, if only for the sake of argument, that detention for some length of time can be justified as what the offender deserves, or as a declaration of society's disapproval, or as the only way of ensuring treatment for a disorder (according to the circumstances, one's moral philosophy, or one's therapeutic optimism). The fuss is about prolongation of the detention beyond the time regarded as required to expiate the crime, declare the disapproval, provide a deterrent, or carry out the treatment.

Of course, in societies which regard very long prison sentences as justified on other grounds, the problem need not be faced. By the time the offender is released, one or more things will have happened. He will be a lot older; and with increasing age everyone's capacity for doing physical harm is increasingly restricted. He will be to some extent institutionalised, which means in this context more compliant with rules, showing less initiative, and less in touch with current facilities – for example, for obtaining firearms illegally. If his violence, or sexual desire, was directed at specific people, such as his wife or daughters, they will probably be beyond his reach by then. If he was simply regarded as a danger to women, or children, or people in general, the public will by the time of his release be frightened of someone else, although it must be granted that alarm is sometimes revived by newspapers whose filing systems are superior to their motives.

What has made the concept of dangerousness a really live issue is the shortening of the periods of detention which legislators, sentencers and psychiatrists regard as justified on other grounds. Whether the retributive approach to sentencing is becoming less prevalent or not, those who still adhere to it seem to be lowering their tariffs. Those who maintain that the fundamental justification for imprisonment is that it declares society's moral values also seem to be using a reduced price list. As for deterrence, we have learned to question the assumption that the difference between a three-year and a ten-year sentence is crucial; and when one reflects that potential offenders are knowledgeable, not to say optimistic, about remission and parole, this is not surprising. Finally, therapeutic claims are now more modest. More and more psychiatrists are prepared to admit that if they cannot produce marked improvements within the first six months of treatment, they will not do so thereafter, however long they try. (' . . . any significant improvement is likely to take place in the first 6 months', says the Department of Health and Social Security in *Review of the Mental Health Act, 1959*.) As for non-psychiatric 'treatment', penologists are increasingly sceptical about its efficacy in dealing with most kinds of law breaking. All of which means that if you want to detain someone for, say, ten years most of that period now has to be justified by the claim that you are protecting others by doing so.

But one may be forgiven for asking what is wrong with that claim. Why shouldn't the protection of the public be regarded as a justification which is quite as sound as retribution, deterrence, or the need for treatment? There is an answer which is based, fundamentally, on the argument that you may have a right to detain someone for something which he *has* done, or at least attempted or risked by his recklessness or negligence, but not for something which he *has not* done but might do. As a Swedish judge once put it to me in conversation, 'you are punishing him for a crime which he hasn't committed'. In this form the argument is clearly retributive, and, what is more, retributive in the traditional Kantian way. Modern retributivism insists that sentences must be restricted to people who break the law with *mens rea*, but does not insist that the nature or length of the sentence must be commensurate with their wickedness. It allows that once you have given the state the right to sentence you, that sentence may be shaped by other aims, such as deterrence or reform; and if by such aims, why not by the aim of protecting others? It is only the traditional retributivist who insists that the form or length of the sentence must be limited by proportionality to one's wickedness.

The Swedish judge's point of view, however, cannot be dismissed simply by labelling it traditional. What has to be pointed out is that it seeks to impose restrictions on the law-enforcement system which we do not impose on other social institutions. The most obvious example is the compulsory commitment of certain mentally disordered people when this is done to protect others. Sometimes they are so disordered that even the most retributive moralist would concede that they are guiltless. But since the detention of the mentally disordered is one of the subjects of this controversy I had better add examples which are not. One is the disqualification of epileptics from driving. Another is the restrictions which we place on people who are known or suspected to carry diseases with a high mortality rate, such as smallpox, typhoid, lassa fever, or Marburg virus. The traditional retributivist, who asserts that the law enforcement system ought not to take account of the harm which people might do, must either explain why it should be subject to a restrictive principle which we do not apply outside the system, or else argue that we should apply the same principle *outside the law enforcement system.*

That may dispose of the retributivist who calls protective measures punishment for uncommitted crimes; but that is not the only objection to protection as a justification. Another extreme one is that we ought never to classify anyone as dangerous, and, therefore, ought never to subject anyone to compulsory measures aimed solely at the safety of others. In its pure form, as we have seen, this argument is sometimes expressed by saying that there are no dangerous people, only dangerous actions. If all that is meant by this is that nobody is ever *certain* to do harm to others in the future, it is acceptable. Something may always intervene, whether it is a change of circumstances or a change of heart. But if it means that we can never say of anyone 'unless something very unlikely happens to prevent him, that man is going to kill or seriously injure somebody within the next year or two', then it goes too far.

After all, we make very confident predictions about other sorts of behaviour. We lend money to people – some people anyway – because we know that unless they drop dead, or are stricken with amnesia, they will pay us back. We assume that people will do what they say they will do, whether they are debtors or terrorists.

It is proper of course to draw a distinction between someone who says, 'I'll pay you back' or 'I'm going to fight for the liberation of my country with bombs and bullets', and on the other hand the sort of prisoner, or patient, who says, 'I don't want to commit another assault (or rape or whatever act brought him inside), but I know that in certain circumstances I won't be able to help myself'. He differs in two ways from the man who declares his intention to do something nasty. First, on the assumption that he is telling the truth about his intentions, he is morally less responsible if he does do it. Second, he is usually less likely to do it, because, whereas the international terrorist will probably try to *make* opportunities for what he is liable to do, the other man is more likely to *avoid* opportunities if he foresees them in time. There are exceptions: some sexual offenders' behaviour is extremely compulsive: but fortunately the compulsive behaviour usually takes relatively harmless forms, such as exhibitionism.

Both these groups, however (that is, those who declare intentions and those who confess their inability to resist impulses or compulsions), must be distinguished from the sort of person who truthfully denies that he is conscious of a desire to repeat what he has done. He may believe that his violence was the natural, even inevitable, outcome of an unusual situation in which he found himself; and it may indeed be the case that this is the only sort of situation in which he has behaved violently. It is this type of case which provides the anti-protectionists with their strongest talking-point. For not only is intentional personal violence by an adult a comparatively rare event (at least in a society which is not at war); it is even rarer for an adult who has been officially identified with such violence to be associated with violence on a later occasion. The same seems to be true of sexual offences which involve the serious molestation of unwilling victims. Reconvictions for violent or serious sexual offences are much rarer than reconvictions for dishonesty or traffic offences: and it is most unlikely that this can be explained to any important extent by differences in reporting rates.

More precisely, not only is there no definable category of violent or sexual offender of whom it can be predicted with certainty that he will do similar harm in the future: there is only one definable category at present of whom this can be predicted with even a high probability: the offender who declares his intention of doing it again. This is in contrast to dishonest offenders: it is not difficult to define groups of men of whom at least two-thirds will be reconvicted of dishonesty within a few years. All one has to do is to define them as males with four or five previous convictions for dishonesty. If you predict of the members of such a group that they will behave dishonestly again, you will be right a good deal more often than wrong. But with violence, it is said, the reverse is the case: nobody has so far reliably defined in this way a group of violent males with a probability of further violence approaching even 50 per cent. In other words, we have not yet succeeded in providing criteria which would ensure that a prediction of future violence would be right more often than it would be wrong. With present criteria, it would more often be wrong.

This being so, the anti-protectionists argue, a period of custody, or an extension of custody, which is imposed solely in order to protect others against violence will be *unnecessarily* imposed in the majority of cases. Put more strongly, it will mean detaining two or three (or even more) individuals in order to prevent only one of them from committing further violence.[1]

This sounds like irresistible arithmetic. But it is arithmetic with limitations. In the first place, it must be pointed out that the attempts to find criteria that would define high-risk groups have not been very thorough. They have been improvised pieces of research based on data which happened to be available. In fairness, it must be said that it is very difficult indeed to design a piece of research which would meet the required standards of thoroughness. The difficulties include the relative infrequency of repeated violence; the very natural unwillingness of penal systems or hospitals to release violent inmates in an experimental way; the lack of reliable information about the situations in which the violence occurred; the still greater lack of information about violence which did not lead to prosecution or admission to hospital. Nevertheless, the likelihood is that a thorough large-scale piece of research, designed specifically for this purpose, would succeed in producing criteria that would enable us to define groups with a future violence rate substantially over 50 per cent, so that we could at least be right more often than we would be wrong. Indeed, there are at least three samples which already support this. Two were collected some years ago by David Steer and myself (Walker, Hammond and Steer, 1967); one was a sample of Scots convicted of violence in the 1950s, the other a sample of Londoners also convicted of violence in the late 1950s. The best, however, is a sample of men convicted of violence or robbery in January 1971 in England or Wales, collected by Phillpotts and Lancucki of the Home Office Statistical Division. In all three samples one variable alone – having four or more previous convictions for violence (or robbery – in the 1971 sample) – was enough to identify a small group of which more than 50 per cent were later convicted of further robbery or violence. Moreover, these reconviction rates take no account of crimes of robbery or violence which some of the offenders may have committed without being convicted. The groups were small in number, but they were identifiable in all three samples. If this could be achieved with the use of only one variable, greater precision should be achievable by using additional information.

The second answer to the anti-protectionist's arithmetic is more fundamental. Let us accept that in our present state of partial ignorance any labelling of the individual as a future perpetrator of violence is going to be mistaken in the majority of cases. Does it follow that it is wrong to apply this label? Only if we swallow two assumptions. One is that it is *morally wrong* to make mistakes of this kind. Everyone would agree that it is *regrettable*; but if the decision is taken with good intentions, and one has done one's best, with the available information, to minimise the percentage of mistaken detentions, is it *morally wrong*? Only if we swallow the second assumption – namely, the anti-protectionist's insistence that our overriding objective must be to minimise the total number of mistaken decisions, treating a mistaken decision to detain as exactly equal to a mistaken decision to release. The anti-protectionist is using two neat rhetorical tricks at once. By referring to mistaken detentions and mistaken releases simply as 'mistakes', he is implying that they all count the same; and by glossing over the difference between 'regrettable' and 'morally wrong' he is implying that it is our moral duty to go for the smallest number of mistakes irrespective of their nature.

To put this point in concrete terms, suppose that you have in custody three men who have done serious violence to more or less innocent victims. Suppose, too, that the best actuarial information you can get tells you that one of them – but not which one – will do more violence if released. The anti-protectionist is saying that it is your moral duty to release all three instead of continuing to detain all three, because release will involve only one mistaken decision instead of two mistaken decisions. Yet the one mistaken release would mean injury or death to someone, while the two mistaken detentions would mean something quite different: the continued deprivation of freedom for three men of whom an unidentifiable two would not do anybody injury if released. It is natural, perhaps even morally right, to look for rules on which to base such difficult decisions; but arithmetic will not make them for us. The most it can do is to give us some idea of the magnitude of the risks involved in each of the choices we are faced with. I shall suggest in a minute what sorts of rules can help us further towards rational decisions, but there are two more anti-arithmetical points to be made.

For another rhetorical technique is to terrify us with large numbers. Dr Megargee, in an otherwise excellent article (1976), asks us to consider what would happen if tests devised by Dr Kozol, which yield only about 50 per cent of false positives, were applied to a random sample of 100,000 citizens. According to Megargee's arithmetic, this would wrongly identify nearly 50,000 people as future perpetrators of violence. This certainly means that, quite apart from morality, the application of such a test to the general population is out of the question on political and economic grounds. But is anyone seriously proposing an exercise of that sort? Surely what we are talking about is not whether we should go out into the streets to round up 50,000 people, but whether we should release, or continue to detain, a much smaller number who are already in our prisons or hospitals.

Another rhetorical use of statistics is the argument that even if we released every man of violence as soon as he had served his just sentence, the resulting increase in crimes of intentional violence would be negligible. This is probably true. The great majority of people convicted of intentional crimes of violence not resulting in homicide are released after a few years; and the release of the remaining minority a few years earlier than they would otherwise have become free would add only a small percentage to the annual total of violent crimes. But this argument implies that because we cannot prevent the great majority of violent crimes we should not try to prevent a few of them. If we reasoned like this, we would never disqualify dangerous drivers.

What might worry us morally would be statistics showing that people whom we are detaining for the protection of others are no more likely to be violent in the future than the man in the street; more precisely, than any other member of the same sex and age-group who has not yet committed violence. (If we had the necessary information we should, of course, add ethnic and occupational groups.) And there *are* one or two categories of violent offenders of whom this is probably true. An example is the parent who puts his or her children to death – intending perhaps to commit suicide as well – while he or she is in a severe depression; or the hitherto non-violent man who kills his wife, or mistress, out of justifiable jealousy. There is scope here for some very relevant research.

But with such exceptions it would be very difficult to argue that the violent people whom we are detaining are no more likely to commit further violence than hitherto non-violent people. In general the evidence strongly suggests, at least so far as males are concerned:

- that each age-group has what we may call its own general probability of behaving with serious violence, which is quite low, though slightly higher for young adults than for older ones;
- but that in each age-group the man who is known to have committed violence once already has a probability which is definitely higher than the general probability; and
- that this probability increases somewhat with each additional known act of violence, although there is almost certainly a ceiling somewhere.

Truly 'nothing predicts behavior like behavior' (Kvaraceus, 1966). In short, with the sort of exceptions I have instanced, it cannot be argued that the violent people whom we detain are no more likely to commit violence in the future than the non-violent man in the street.

Non-Arithmetical Rules

But what sort of non-arithmetical rules would help in deciding when to apply purely protective measures? I can, as I promised, offer a few. They do not have the spurious precision of the arithmetic just discussed: in the last analysis they are an appeal to values.

(1) The first is concerned with the sort of harm to which we should limit such measures. I suggest that when the measures involve serious and lasting hardship for the persons to whom we apply them – as any form of detention does – they should be used only to prevent serious and lasting hardship to other individuals, of a kind which, once caused, cannot be remedied. Since most loss of or damage to property can be remedied by compensation, whether by the offender, insurance, or the state, this rule excludes all or nearly all property offences (one can have an argument, however, about the theft or damage of unique works of art). It excludes temporary alarm (such as that caused by an imitation or unloaded pistol) and minor affronts to decency, such as exhibitionism. It *includes*, however, lasting psychological harm as well as disabling or disfiguring physical injury; so that rape, blackmail, kidnapping would be included. Nor does the rule insist that the harm must actually have been done; if the offender intended the harm or must have realised that it was a highly probable result of what he did or attempted, he should come within the rule.

(2) The second rule is that there should be good reason to believe that the actions to which the first rule applies were not an isolated, out-of-character episode so far as the individual offender was concerned. Similar conduct on two or more occasions, separated by substantial periods of time, would be good reason to believe this; so would a declared intention, such as vengeance on the members of a family.

(3) The third rule, however, is that if it can be reasonably argued that the circumstances which provided the offender with his incentive have ceased to exist (for example, through the death of his enemies), or that for some other reason (such as incapacity) he is unlikely to repeat his behaviour, this argument must operate in his favour. This rule will sound fairly uncontroversial, until I argue that it should also apply, though not invariably, to an offender's first experience of compulsory detention. In plain terms, if for the offence which brings him within the scope of Rule 1 the offender has been sentenced to imprisonment or otherwise compulsorily detained for the first time in his life, it can be reasonably argued that this experience will make him less likely to repeat his behaviour. Of course, there will be obvious exceptions; for instance, the man who after a year or two inside still says, 'The first thing I'm going to do when I get out is to finish him off properly this time'. Again, someone who has already experienced imprisonment (or its equivalent) for some quite different behaviour, such as mere theft, would not benefit from this rule. But with such exceptions

the first period of compulsory detention should not, for the sole purpose of protecting others, be made longer than it would otherwise have been.

(4) The fourth rule is that if any less drastic measure than detention offers a reasonable prospect of protecting others, it should be used instead. In some cases supervision offers this prospect, especially when coupled with sensible requirements (such as residence at a specified address) or with prohibitions (for example, someone who has acted as an enforcer for a protection racket, and whose face is well known to the local police, could be forbidden to enter certain parts of a city). People could be disqualified from doing certain jobs – for instance, those involving responsibility for children. It is true that to some people the idea of strict supervision is objectionable, and not merely because of its practical difficulty. They regard it as too burdensome, or as incompatible with freedom. Most offenders, however, prefer conditional freedom to detention, even if they make things difficult for their supervisors. Doctrinaire objectors to strict supervision must face the fact that they are making it more difficult for courts to shorten prison sentences, or to consider non-custodial precautions, and more difficult for parole authorities to release dangerous offenders.

(5) The fifth, and last, rule is that if you feel justified in detaining someone or prolonging his detention solely for the safety of others, the conditions of his detention should be made as tolerable as possible. The force of this rule, like that of the others, is a moral one. When the detention is no longer justifiable as retribution, denunciation, deterrence, or correction, but solely as a protection for others, its conditions should be no worse, apart from the deprivation of liberty, than those which a law-abiding wage-earner would enjoy outside. This is, of course, an idealistic standard to set, and there is scope here for a great deal of detailed discussion and ingenuity; all that can be stated here is the principle.

Who Should Decide What?

Who is to apply these rules? To some extent the answer must vary according to the structure of a society's law enforcement system, and according to the degree of trust which its members have in their police, in their courts and their advisers, and in the administrators and staffs of their prisons and hospitals. Unless this trust is complete, however – and it never should be – the limits of protective sentencing must be set by the legislature. The form of the sentence and the circumstances in which a person should be eligible for it are matters for legislation. On the other hand, legislation should not attempt to define circumstances in which a protective measure *must* be imposed. It should always be possible for a human being, whether acting as a sentencer or in some other capacity, to say, 'The law allows a protective measure in this case, but it does not seem necessary'. Except where murder is concerned, most modern legislation takes this form.

The difficulties of drafting a legal definition of eligibility can be exaggerated, especially if one makes the mistake of trying to define the circumstances in which a protective measure *must* be used. As has just been said, the most that legislation should attempt is a definition of circumstances in which it *may* be used, leaving the sentencer or the psychiatric authority, as the case may be, the discretion *not* to use it. Once this approach is adopted, the difficulties diminish. It is not impossible to draw up a list of criminal offences to which protective measures should be restricted.[2] This is the solution adopted in several penal codes. It is not impossible to stipulate that evidence must be provided that there is a substantial probability that the offender will, if not prevented, behave in a similarly harmful way in the future. There are, of course, special legal problems in compulsory commitment to mental hospitals or juvenile institutions, especially when this can be arranged without the authority of a court; but one attractive solution would be to enact that nobody, whether adult or not, sane or not, can be detained solely for the protection of others without the express authority of a court, again requiring the court to be satisfied about the probability of future similar behaviour.

But is a court the best authority to exercise this discretion? I am not suggesting that we remove sentencing from the functions of criminal courts. What I have suggested elsewhere (1969) is that a court which thinks it has a case for a protective sentence should not have the final say in the matter: only the power to remit the case to a special tribunal. (It should be possible to appeal against the decision to remit the case to the tribunal.) This would have two advantages. It would limit courts to the functions of sentencing for deterrent, corrective, even retributive or denunciatory purposes, thus making it clear that the protection of society is not the function of an ordinary sentence. (But when remitting the case, the court could indicate what sentence it would have imposed if the need for protecting others had not arisen.)

Secondly, since the occasions on which a protective sentence is justified are rare, so that few if any ordinary courts encounter enough of them to build up any experience worth the name, it would ensure that these cases come before an authority which would specialise in them, which could be given a set of guiding rules (not necessarily in statutory language) and which could both initiate research and apply its results. The tribunal would have power to decide on less drastic measures than detention in suitable cases. It should be clear that this proposal is based on the assertion not that courts are incompetent at sentencing, but that protective measures should be sharply distinguished from ordinary sentences.

The Form of Sentence

It is the *form* of the custodial sentence, however, which arouses the sharpest disagreement. Not only anti-protectionists but even some people who accept the need for occasional sentences of protective length argue that it is unnecessary, or even undesirable, to legislate for a special kind of sentence. Unnecessary because, they argue, courts have sufficient scope, within the maxima set by law, to increase the length of a sentence with protection in view. Undesirable, because the existence of a special sentence would encourage courts to use it, as is said to have happened in the USA. The argument that it is unnecessary holds only in jurisdictions where four conditions are fulfilled: high permissible maxima for all the relevant kinds of offences, express authority in statute or case-law to add to the normal length of a prison sentence in order to protect others, an obligation on sentencers to declare when they are using imprisonment in this way, and the possibility of appeals against such use. The argument that the existence of a special sentence would make it too popular with sentencers is not borne out by experience, or at least by experience in some countries. In Denmark the well thought-out and well-drafted revision of the *forvaring* (protective sentence) statutes did not lead to a marked increase in its use: indeterminate protective sentences are too unpopular there, as they are in Scandinavia as a whole. In England successive efforts to offer judges an extended form of sentence for persistent (not necessarily dangerous) offenders have failed: temporary enthusiasm for each new offer was followed by virtual disuse. The use of 'life' as a discretionary sentence for dangerous offenders has been strictly limited by English case-law – that is, judge-made law – to offenders who are mentally unstable.

In favour of a special form of sentence for the dangerous are two powerful considerations. It compels sentencers to make it clear when they are trying to protect the public. In England it is too easy for a judge to add a few years on to the prison term he would otherwise have chosen, so long as he keeps within the legal maximum and the normal range. He may or may not say expressly that he has done so in order to protect others: if he does not, it is very difficult to appeal against the sentence on the ground that it is unnecessarily protective. The second advantage is that a special protective sentence can have special provisions designed with dangerousness in view: an obvious example is after-care arrangements.

But the most important problem is clearly the method of selection of a release date. How should this be done? This question is best approached indirectly, by asking easier questions first. At what stage should release be decided upon? Who should have the final say? The answers to these will at least exclude certain possible forms of sentence. For example, it is very difficult to argue that the exact duration of protective detention should be determined at the time of first sentencing. This makes sense only when the aim of a sentence is deterrence, denunciation, deserved punishment, or correction. When the aim is the protection of others, the date of release must logically be determined at a later stage. Once this is recognised, the question whether the date should be determined by a court of law or by some other agency becomes much more open to discussion. In countries with parole boards the function of deciding, or at least recommending, release dates usually falls to them; but both the theory and practice of parole are under attack these days. In France, some sentences are reviewable by a judge who is not the sentencing judge; but this system, too, is open to criticisms, of which the most obvious is that a single person, who is also a career judge, is not the best qualified or most objective of arbiters. If my proposal for a specialised authority were adopted, it would be desirable, though not logically necessary, to entrust it with this function.

If that proposal is rejected, however, an authority resembling a parole board seems preferable to a judicial authority. When the question at issue is not distributive justice, desert, denunciation, or deterrence, but whether an offender is less likely than he was to do harm, what is needed are not legal qualifications, but a combination of several kinds of expertise. The chief criticism levelled against parole boards is that they tend to 'resentence' individuals on the basis of much the same information as was before the original sentencer. Whether this is so is very questionable; but even if it were true, we need not accept the implication that resentencing is necessarily a bad thing: some sentences are all the better for reconsideration when feelings have died down. But that is a digression: what we are considering is an entirely different sort of decision, to which the considerations involved in ordinary sentencing are to be irrelevant.

If this is granted, it seems to follow that a determinate sentence has little if anything to recommend it. If short, it may be too short, so that the staff of an institution have to release a man who is as dangerous as when he arrived. If long, it may be too long. Even if a long sentence carries a built-in possibility of release before the due date, the sheer length of it can have two undesirable results. One is that it may influence the releasing authority, the other is that it may demoralise the offender.

There are also objections to a completely indeterminate sentence, such as the 'life' sentence. It is said to be even more demoralising than a long determinate sentence, because it offers not even a distant guarantee of freedom. The extent to which this generalisation is justified must depend partly on the personality of the lifer himself, partly on what offenders believe to be the likely period of detention under such a sentence. In North America life sentences frequently mean twenty years inside; in Sweden the indeterminate protective sentence usually leads to conditional release within three or four years. In Britain lifers are usually released after eight, nine or ten years, but the period varies from one to twenty years at the extremes, so that a lifer who reaches his eighth or ninth year without being promised a release date is likely to become very anxious or depressed.

Complete indeterminancy is not the only alternative, however, to a so-called determinate sentence. One possibility is a sentence which must be reviewed at short intervals; a Canadian Bill adopted this solution. Two British committees – the Scottish Council on Crime and the Butler Committee on Mentally Abnormal Offenders – have recommended it. Its essential feature is the statutory insistence on regular review, at which the case for further detention, rather than the case for release, has to be made. It can also incorporate compulsory post-release supervision, again with regular review.

Another possibility – adopted in the Netherlands – is a renewable sentence. This would be a sentence of a length fixed in accordance with ordinary sentencing considerations, which was expressly subject to review not long before its termination, at which stage the reviewing body would be permitted to make a case to a court for a limited extension. If it did not make such a case, or if the court was not convinced by the case, the offender would automatically be released. This has the attraction that it makes detention solely for public protection impossible without the continuing concurrence both of experts and of the judiciary.

Any solution – apart from one which simply rules out protective sentencing – is open to the objection that it is difficult for those who have charge of dangerous offenders in conditions of captivity to tell, on the basis of hard facts, whether a man is any less likely to repeat his harmful behaviour when he is not in captivity. The problem can be, and sometimes is, exaggerated. There are cases in which changed circumstances, attitudes, or physical capacity clearly reduce the likelihood of repetition. In any case, the problem can be diminished by more flexible systems of provisional release and by thorough investigation (and in some cases control) of the conditions under which the offender will be living when released. And since the problem is shared by all constructive solutions it cannot be an objection to any of them.

Detention without Trial

What I have been saying until now may have sounded as if I had in mind only dangerous offenders who are tried and sentenced. In fact I have not overlooked the problem of compulsory commitment to mental hospitals without trial; and my five rules are as applicable to them as to any convicted offender. Nevertheless, patients do pose two distinct problems. One is the procedural question: how do we safeguard them against unwarranted detention beyond the stage at which they cease to improve under treatment? The nature and effectiveness of safeguards varies so much from one jurisdiction to another that detailed proposals could be worked out only in each different context. But the general principle, I suggest, must be that the need to detain any involuntary patient beyond six months should be reviewed at regular intervals (without the necessity for an application by the patient) by some authoritative body of people who are all completely independent of the hospital in which the patient is detained. (It should also be the function of that body to make sure that any long-term patient who is said to be a voluntary inmate really is voluntary.) The reviewing members should include a lawyer, a social worker and a psychiatrist. The member whose position will be most difficult will, of course, be the psychiatrist, because the cohesiveness of his profession will sometimes mean that a decision to order release will be embarrassing for him. In order to lessen this difficulty, the decision should be by a confidential vote, so that his colleagues need not know whether he voted for or against it; and there should always be enough non-psychiatrists to outvote the psychiatrists.

There would be some advantages in the proposal that a person regarded as dangerous should always be prosecuted, so that what he has actually done could be subjected to the thorough scrutiny of a criminal court. Even the Butler Committee in England, which recommended that the prosecution of the mentally disordered should be avoided unless there were strong reasons for it, expressly said that dangerousness is a strong reason. But while this is a fairly sound principle, it would not solve some problems. In particular, it would not deal with the patient who has not actually done or attempted anything that could have resulted in serious harm, but has merely talked about doing it. An example which is bound to occur to everyone is the paranoid man who regards the head of state or some other important person as the source of his persecution, and who says that if the persecution does not stop he will kill him. In many jurisdictions he would have committed no criminal offence. It is all very well to compel him to enter hospital for treatment; but what do we do when the psychiatrists have done their best by way of therapy, and the only justification for further detention is that he might still do what he has talked of doing? Should we release him and keep an eye on him to see whether he tries to acquire a firearm or manufacture a letter-bomb? Should we detain him on the grounds that someone who talks about killing presents a sufficient danger? The only solution seems to me to be a reviewing authority of the kind I have been describing.

Having argued throughout this chapter that it is defensible from the moral point of view to detain, or otherwise control, certain people for the protection of others, and that from the legal point of view it is not impossible to draft provisions for this purpose with satisfactory safeguards, I want to redress the balance with two final points. One is that so far as this problem is concerned no system of rules can avoid the need for decisions by human beings, with all their biases and irrational fears. The other is that custodial institutions, however liberally managed, are places of last resort, whether for the mentally ill or for offenders. There are a few people so handicapped that they find institutional life more tolerable than what we call 'life in the community'; and then it is usually because they have no community, or none that will accept them. But with these exceptions, to dispose of someone in this way is to deprive him of much that makes life worth living. Almost any degree of non-custodial control is preferable.

Summary

The main points I have been making are these. The difficulties of defining dangerousness have been exaggerated: we do it in practice every day. The objections to labelling people as dangerous are no greater than the objections to labelling them 'loyal' or 'deceitful'. What is debatable is what we are justified in doing to dangerous people by way of incapacitation; and what particularly needs justification in the case of offenders is their detention for longer than other penal aims require. But to condemn this as punishing people for crimes not yet committed is an oversimplification. The arithmetical arguments of the anti-protectionists are also rhetorical rather than sound. On the other hand, the use of detention to incapacitate the dangerous offender should be subject to the five rules which I have outlined.

The difficulties of drafting legislation can also be exaggerated, especially if it is assumed that the law should try to define circumstances in which special sentences must be imposed. All it should attempt is to set fairly strict limits to the use of such a sentence. The decision to use it or not in a given case should ideally be taken by a special tribunal to which courts could refer prima facie cases: this would have several advantages. As for the form which the sentence should take, there are strong objections both to sentences of fixed length and completely indeterminate detention. These are not, however, the only possibilities: others are the reviewable and the renewable sentence.

The detention of mentally disordered offenders for the sake of others raises one special problem. A rule that this should never be done without prosecution – that is, never under civil procedure – would prevent most abuses. An awkwardness is the rare case in which a disordered person seems to be talking seriously about killing (or seriously harming) others. Apart from the anti-protectionists's course – to do nothing – all that can be done to prevent undue detention in such cases is to have them reviewed frequently by a competent authority.

The most important rule of all, however, is that detention is a last resort: any kind of non-custodial measure, however much of a nuisance, should be considered first.

Notes: Chapter 3

1   For a strongly argued example of the anti-protectionist case see Professor A. E. Bottoms's Inaugural Lecture 'Reflections on the renaissance of dangerousness' (Bottoms, 1977).
2   The more detailed the subdivision of wrongdoing in the criminal code, the more effective this will be in excluding the sorts of behaviour against which we do not demand protection. Conversely, a vague code, which, for example, labelled as rape not only a violent assault on an unwilling woman but also intercourse with a girl just under the age of consent, will make such a list open to misuse.

The text of this contribution has already been published in the author's book *Punishment, Danger and Stigma* (1980), and is reproduced here (with some minor modifications) by permission of Blackwells, Oxford.

4 Indefinite Detention: Hospitalisation Criteria

CHRISTOPHER TREVES BROWN

In the introduction to his essay 'On Liberty', published in 1859, John Stuart Mill wrote:

> The object of this essay is to assert one very simple principle. That principle is that the sole end for which mankind is warranted, individually or collectively, in interfering with the liberty of action of any of their number, is self-protection. That the only purpose for which power can be rightfully exercised over any member of a civilised community against his will, is to prevent harm to others. His own good, either physical or moral, is not a sufficient warrant.

However, under the United Kingdom Mental Health Act (1959) which allows for indefinite detention, a civil patient can be detained for observation for twenty-eight days because (assuming that other conditions are also satisfied) 'he ought to be so detained in the interests of his own health or safety or with a view to the protection of others' (section 25). Compulsory admission for treatment for up to a year requires that a similar criterion be satisfied, but with a slight change in wording, 'that it is necessary in the interests of the patient's health and safety or for the protection of other persons that the patient should be so detained'. Mill would not have liked the Mental Health Act.

Is Mill's utilitarian view appropriate to all individuals? He, himself, excluded children, on the ground that they need protection because of their immaturity, but he did not consider the position for those who have outgrown the state of needing protection but later revert to it.

In recent years, controversy over compulsory hospitalisation on medical grounds has focused on its use in the mental health field, but doctors have long had the power, sometimes on their own authority alone, to detain patients suffering from a wide variety of illnesses. For instance, in Queen Victoria's reign, the Contagious Diseases Acts of 1864 and 1866 authorised the detention, in hospital, of prostitutes infected with venereal disease. In 1864 the army and navy chiefs had set up a committee 'to enquire into the pathology and treatment of the venereal disease, with a view to diminishing its injurious effects upon the men of the army and navy'. There is no doubt that the main motive for setting up the committee was to control the incidence of venereal disease which was seriously reducing the number of soldiers and sailors fit enough to do their jobs. Even so, the committee's report also referred to the welfare of the prostitutes and their (the committee's) surprise that, in general, the prostitutes welcomed the controls introduced by the 1864 Act.

Another example is the Poor Law Amendment Act (1867) which included a section 'authorising the detention of any person already in a workhouse who was suffering from mental disease or from bodily disease of an infectious or contagious character' if the medical officer of the workhouse reported that the patient was not in a proper state to leave the workhouse without danger to himself or others (Report of the Royal Commission, 1908, paragraph 206 quoting the 1867 Act). More recently, the Public Health Act (1936) laid down the circumstances under which patients with specified notifiable diseases could be detained compulsorily. The National Assistance Act (1948) and the National Assistance (Amendment) Act of 1951 still allow compulsory admission to hospital or other suitable accommodation, of 'persons who a) are suffering from grave chronic disease or, being aged, infirm or physically incapacitated, are living in insanitary conditions and b) are unable to devote to themselves, and are not receiving from other persons proper care and attention'.

On the whole, apart from the National Assistance Act (whose powers of compulsory hospitalisation are probably seldom used – see Forster and Tiplady, 1980, and subsequent correspondence) the beneficiaries of the compulsory procedures are the public who, but for the compulsory removal of the affected persons, might become similarly affected. The same could be said to apply to the National Assistance Act if it is assumed that neighbours of people living in insanitary conditions fear for their own health and amenity. It can therefore be said that the law tries to stick to the principle stated by Mill.

However, sometimes a strict utilitarian view causes difficulties, a good example being the reason for the 1951 Amendment of the 1948 National Assistance Act. Section 47 of the 1948 Act is the one concerned with compulsory hospitalisation. The procedure was for the local authority, acting on medical advice, to apply to the court for an order authorising the compulsory removal of the person considered to be in need of care and protection. Seven days' notice that the application to the court had been made had to be given before the court hearing took place. The 1951 Amendment Act was introduced by a medically qualified Member of Parliament one of whose elderly constituents fell and refused to go to hospital. She remained on the floor for the full seven days, at the end of which she had developed a pressure sore and tetanus from which, when she was finally admitted to hospital, she soon died (Muir Gray, 1980). Under the 1951 Act, the seven days' notice could be dispensed with if two doctors certified 'that, in their opinion, it is necessary in the interests of [the patient] to remove him without delay'.

The National Assistance Acts of 1948 and 1951 are thus an example of the telescoping of the administrative procedures which were intended to protect an unwilling patient, for the benefit of that same patient. Legislation may, therefore, reflect a less utilitarian view in practice than theory would suggest that it should. The point is important, for it introduces a sub-jective element into the attitude of law-makers, which, in turn, means that public opinion on when (or even if) compulsory hospitalisation is legitimate will vary between different groups of people and between different periods of time. And it is difficult for any of us to recognise how much our individual attitudes are moulded by current public opinion and philosophy.

An important example of the significance of public opinion was pointed out by the Royal Commission on the law relating to mental disorder, whose report was published in 1954 and led to the Mental Health Act of 1959. They say (paragraph 211): 'Powers of detention in the eyes of most people today are objectionable in principle . . . . At the beginning of this century, social reformers with the interests of the mentally disordered at heart, con-sidered certification a privilege . . . . This is abundantly clear throughout the Report of the Royal Commission on the Care and Control of the Feeble Minded' (HMSO, 1908). An echo of the attitude of the 1908 report may have taken place during the economic depression of the 1930s. Indigent patients may then have been taken into hospital compulsorily (voluntary admission being then unavailable to them) as a kindness to them simply because of their indigence. Many of such patients have spent most of a life-time in mental deficiency institutions having, in essence, the same sheltered accommodation and employment within the hospital which, under current conditions, they would probably have had outside. Put more crudely, doctors bent the rules for what they would claim to be humani-tarian reasons.

This leads to the question of admission to hospital for social reasons. Some of the published literature on this subject is referred to later in this chapter. Here, it seems right to state that most of us, in clinical practice, offer hospital accommodation on what amounts to social grounds, although we may prefer to have some medical justification for our action, however flimsy that justification may seem to be, objectively. Further-more, all of us must have patients in our in-patient units who, having been admitted for medical reasons, remain in hospital long after the medical problems are resolved because they are otherwise homeless. The most extreme form of the social admission is the short-stay admission of chronic patients, suffering from a wide range of disabilities, in order to give a break in routine to those who normally care for the patients in the community. With such holiday relief patients, there may be no advantage to the patient at all; the object of the exercise is to help someone else.

Is there a clear distinction between voluntary and compulsory pro-cedures? Muir Gray (1980), predicting the effect of the repeal of section 47 of the National Assistance Act, writes:

I believe that the old people would continue to be compulsorily removed as at present, and would not necessarily be left at home to die in freedom, albeit cold and squalid freedom. Most would eventually be coerced, deceived, drugged or 'persuaded' into homes or hospitals as many elderly people already are. I believe . . . that elderly people often 'give in' under sustained pressure exerted by relatives, friends and professionals.

In the mental health field, the threat that compulsory sanctions may be invoked is used to encourage reluctant patients to accept treatment informally. Such a process might seem to an outsider to be compulsory in all but name.

Apart from the Mental Health Act, most compulsory hospitalisations involve the magistracy at some stage. Presumably the reason for this is, nowadays, to protect the civil liberties of the patient. In order for this protection to be real, the magistrate must evaluate a medical decision. As the magistrate is normally non-medical, it may well be rather naïve to assume that a magistrate would ever refuse a strong and well-presented medical case.

An additional point about the involvement of the magistracy in the field of compulsory hospitalisation on mental health grounds is mentioned by the 1954 Royal Commission report. This is the question of whether the justices of the peace were originally involved in admission procedures for administrative rather than judicial reasons. Put very simply, this arrangement would hold that the justices were responsible for establishing and running the early mental hospitals and, as such, were custodians of the public purse. By signing an order for the detention of a patient in a mental hospital, they would not, then, be lending judicial approval to a temporary denial of the patient's civil liberty so much as acknowledging that the patient was one on whom public money could reasonably be spent. After discussing the case for taking this view, the Royal Commission report goes on: 'and whatever the origin of the Justice's Order in the nineteenth century, in the twentieth it has certainly come to be regarded as judicial in intent' (paragraph 265). This is the context in which it must now be considered, both in the mental health field and in those other fields in which compulsory procedures are applied.

This, then, is some of the background to any consideration of compulsory procedures on mental health grounds, and can be summarised as follows: First, however much those who make or interpret the law may try to stick to the view that compulsion should not be used for a patient's own good, in practice the good of the patient, as perceived by those implementing the legislation, is often considered. Secondly, compulsion is available in several fields of medical practice, so that, in searching for some general principles, one should not look at mental health only. Thirdly, public opinion greatly influences the way legislation is written, and its subsequent interpretation. One could add, here, that there may well be differences in public opinion in different parts of the UK; and even wider ones between different parts of, say, the United States of America. Furthermore, suicide remains a crime in America and different states are able to interpret in different ways words like 'insanity'. Consequently, it is difficult to know how much, if any, of the American literature has any relevance to the British situation. Fourthly, the involvement of the magistracy, though common and possibly obliging the doctors to take serious note of what they are proposing, may nevertheless seem to an outsider to be little more than a ritual window-dressing exercise, unless in a substantial number of cases the medical recommendation is rejected.

Non-Medical Factors Affecting Hospital Admissions

The next part of this chapter takes note of these non-medical factors associated with admission to hospital which have been studied and reported in recent years.

The significance of those non-medical factors in the reasons for the admission of any patient to any hospital varied considerably. At one extreme, one can imagine an acute surgical emergency in which immediate admission to hospital is required and in which non-medical factors seem of little importance. At the other extreme are those admissions in which the person who is admitted to hospital gets no benefit whatever from the admission, which is arranged purely in order to allow the usual caring personnel to have a holiday from that responsibility. Between these extremes, however, a range of non-medical factors come into play.

Environmental Factors

Investigators in Pennsylvania found that more patients were admitted to state institutions during the hot summer months than during the winter. Geographical proximity to a mental hospital increases the chances of admission to it. The general level of economic activity in society at large also affects the mental hospital admission rate. According to Hollingshead and Redlich (1958) there is a changing incidence of psychiatric disorder as one descends the social scale, namely, an increasing incidence of treated psychotic patients, and a decreasing incidence of treated neurotic patients. There is also a variation between social classes in the type of treatment that is given.

More recently, Rushing (1969) has drawn attention to the way in which socio-economic resources protect individuals from incurring society's displeasure in a way that tends to lead to hospitalisation.

Appleyard (1970) reviewed some of the social factors influencing the hospitalisation of children. Housing, the mother's competence and the availability of health insurance policies were all found to be important. Other related factors are the self-confidence of the various doctors involved, their workloads and the availability of hospital resources. Appleyard comments: 'A social admission is not a common diagnostic label, though . . . the reluctance to recognise the importance of social factors is gradually disappearing.'

Family Attitude

Increasing attention has recently been paid to this area. A review article in 1974 (Kreisman and Joy) drew attention to the effect of family attitudes. Leon and Micklin (1978) in an article entitled 'Who shall be hospitalised?' say: 'The opinion of the informant (usually a relative) as to whether the patient is sane or not shows a significant association with the type of care, with 75 per cent of the hospitalised cases, 47 per cent of the outpatients . . . being regarded as psychotic by the relative providing the information.' They go on: 'The significant association between the opinions of the relative . . . and the type of care received by the patient, emphasises the potential influence of family attitudes on the measures taken for handling mental disorders.'

The Selection Process

Assuming a patient gets to a hospital where he is examined with a view to admission, what determines whether he will be admitted or not? Mischler and Waxler (1963) found four variables, namely: whether the referring person was a doctor; whether a relative of the patient was mentioned at the time of the initial request for hospital accommodation; the age of the patient; and whether the patient had previously been hospitalised. In a later paper (Waxler and Mischler, 1963), the same authors refer to the doctor–patient relationship, describing two such relationships, which they call 'physician-centred' and 'family-centred' influence patterns. In the former type, the physician is dominant and assumes full responsibility for the decision to hospitalise or not; whereas in the family-centred pattern, the decision on admission is arrived at with much more influence from the patient's relatives. Physician-centred interviews tended to result in higher incidence of hospitalisation.

Mendel and Rapport (1969) found that the past history of the patient and the identity of the decision-makers were rather more important than the patients themselves. 'In this study, the decision for or against hospitalisation does not seem to be based on clinical factors, but rather on social and attitudinal factors some of which influenced the decision-makers even though they were unaware of such influence.'

More recently, Feigelson *et al.* (1978) arrived at a similar conclusion. For them, 'The severity of a patient's illness . . . played the most important role in the decision to hospitalise', but 'the service facilities appeared to contribute at least as much to the explained variance in hospitalisation when severity and clinical variables were controlled'. On looking at why some hospitals admitted more than others, they noted that the lowest hospitalisation rates occurred in hospitals whose emergency rooms were staffed by attending psychiatrists, whereas the hospitals staffed by psychiatric residents had higher admission rates. Similarly, Mendel and Rapport (1969) had found that decision-makers with less than six months' experience admitted to hospital a significantly larger number of patients than those who had at least three years' experience.

Personal Factors

(1) *Age and sex differences.* Krianciunas (1969) related age and sex to five possible reasons for admission (patient's wish; management difficulties; outwardly directed aggression; inwardly directed aggression; others, incuding alcoholism). Management difficulties tended to be more important in the elderly, but outwardly directed violence was more common in men of all ages and in women in the 20 to 44 age-group.

(2) *Behaviour.*   Frequently an incident which precipitates admission is, objectively, very similar to many incidents in the past. The precipitating

event is thus a 'last straw' which leads to the patient's relatives demanding his admission to hospital. Holmes and Solomon (1980), looking from a different perspective on what may be the same phenomenon, found that 'the presence of bizarre behaviour helps to explain the decision to readmit, but not to first admit. It may be interpreted as an indication of the recurrence of the disorder. Whereas, among the first admissions, it may be viewed as something that will not develop to a more . . . disabling state, or it may be assessed as a problem that can be treated on an outpatient basis.' According to Smith, Pomphrey and Hall (1963) danger to self or others, socially unacceptable behaviour, or illness requiring treatment are three different types of 'last straw' behaviour.

Medical Attitudes

Bourne (1976) believes that the general practitioner's own psycho-pathology is often a determining factor leading to referral by him of a patient for a consultation with a psychiatrist, and Balint (quoted by Courtenay, 1973) has stressed that disturbance occurs in the doctor at the point where there is similarity between his own unsolved problems and those of his patient.

Leon and Micklin (1978) also tried to examine the significance of doctors' attitudes, and noted that patients who interested the doctor or for whom he felt pity were more likely to be admitted to hospital. Patients for whom the doctors' predominant feeling was a desire to help were much more likely to be out-patients.

Summary

Geographical, climatic and economic factors affect hospitalisation rates. Social class and occupation affect whether a person's behaviour is appraised as abnormal and, if it is, whether it should be handled by doctors or lawyers. Family attitudes to misbehaviour affect the level of tolerance within the family and whether the deviant person is to be regarded as a patient.

Once the patient has been deemed abnormal and sent for psychiatric evaluation, the chances of his being hospitalised vary according to the experience and expertise of the doctor or other personnel whom the patient may meet. The severity of psychiatric symptoms are important, but so are the facilities offered by the hospital and such apparently unrelated factors as whether the patient has been hospitalised before. Probably embarrassment at a relative's misbehaviour in public is relevant in that it encourages patients' families to regard hospitalisation as the proper solution to any problems the patient is causing.

Finally, the point may be made that many of the research studies on how and why doctors decide to admit patients to hospital have been conducted by sociologists. Doctors, themselves, seem much less interested in the matter, apart from doctors in administrative posts who need to predict the level of future demand which they must meet.

Special Hospital Admission: Statistical Evidence

The next section of this chapter is an examination of figures for the numbers of patients admitted to the Special Hospitals in England and Wales during the 1960s, when there were three such hospitals.

The Special Hospitals exist for those who 'require treatment under conditions of special security on account of their dangerous, violent or criminal propensities' (Mental Health Act 1959, section 97; also National Health Service Act 1977). That phrase must represent the legal criteria for admission to these hospitals. However, the earlier part of this chapter has sought to show that a range of non-medical factors enter into a decision to admit a patient to other types of hospital. It would be remarkable if those other features were not also operative in admissions to Special Hospitals.

All Special Hospital patients are detained compulsorily, the majority under the Mental Health Act. About half the patients will have committed an offence and been admitted directly from court, but some are transferred to a Special Hospital from a general psychiatric or mental handicap hospital because some aspect of their behaviour puts them beyond the ability of the referring hospital to care for them.

The Mental Health Act (section 4) classifies four types of mental disorder: Mental Illness, Psychopathic Disorder, Subnormality and Severe Subnormality. For a civil patient to be detained for treatment (section 26) or for offender patients held under compulsory powers, the medical certificates must specify from which of the four possible mental disorders the patient is suffering.

Table 4.1 shows the total number of male admissions to the Special Hospitals according to their MHA classification for the years 1961 to 1970. For simplicity, the years have been grouped into two five-year periods, 1961 to 1965 and 1966 to 1970.

Table 4.1   *Total Male Admissions for Two Five-Year Periods According to MHA Classification*

MHA classification	1961–5	1966–70	% change	Totals
Mental Illness	352	530	+51	882
Psychopathic Disorder	234	409	+75	643
Subnormality	216	218	+ 1	434
Severe Subnormality	76	88	+16	164
Combination of above classifications	106	110	+ 4	216
	984	1,355	+38	2,339

Table 4.1 shows that, in the second half of the decade, there were 371 more male admissions than there were in the first half, and that the increase (of 38 per cent of the 1961–5 figure) was almost entirely restricted to patients with the MHA classifications of Mental Illness and Psychopathic Disorder.

The three main sources of admission for Special Hospital patients are the courts, the penal system and the National Health Service, and Table 4.2 shows the total male admissions from each of these sources.

Table 4.2 *Total Male Admissions for Two Five-Year Periods According to the Source of Admission*

Source of admission	1961–5	1966–70	% change	Totals
Direct from court	461	770	+67·0	1,231
Transfer from penal system	158	162	+ 2·5	320
Transfer from NHS hospitals	245	301	+23·0	546
Others	120	122	+ 2·0	242
	984	1,355	+38·0	2,339

Table 4.2 shows that the greater part of the increase of 371 male admissions was in patients admitted direct from the courts, with another large contribution from patients transferred from NHS hospitals.

Table 4.3 shows the rate of referral of potential Special Hospital patients from the fifteen regions of England and Wales whose hospital services were administered by the fifteen Regional Hospital Boards. As Table 4.1 has shown that the increase in admissions over the 1960s was largely restricted to patients with the MHA classifications of Mental Illness and Psychopathic Disorder, Table 4.3 is primarily concerned with those patients.

Table 4.3 *Special Hospital Admission Rates for the Fifteen Regional Hospital Board Areas of England and Wales (per million over five-year period)*

Region	Mental Illness		Psychopathic Disorders		All classifications	
	1961–5	1966–70	1961–5	1966–70	1961–5	1966–70
Northern	1	5·9	13·2	5·9	15·1	30·9	43·5
Yorks.	2	14·1	17·3	8·3	21·8	27·0	55·2
Trent	3	10·5	22·3	6·6	25·0	30·2	68·7
E. Anglia	4	11·6	12·7	13·9	15·0	32·4	33·5
N.W. Thames	5	21·6	30·4	15·2	22·6	60·4	66·8
N.E. Thames	6	16·9	22·9	9·7	14·5	39·8	39·5
S.E. Thames	7	10·7	20·8	11·9	21·4	44·0	64·5
S.W. Thames	8	31·9	52·7	16·9	16·3	70·3	84·0
Wessex	9	11·6	25·3	15·8	14·8	32·7	59·1
Oxford	10	20·9	23·5	12·1	22·2	56·0	77·9
S. West	11	10·6	11·3	3·8	22·6	31·7	55·1
W. Midlands	12	16·2	24·2	9·9	9·9	52·3	61·0
Mersey	13	10·5	12·8	4·5	10·5	22·4	29·2
N. West	14	13·7	19·2	10·1	15·6	48·5	54·0
Wales	15	13·7	22·2	8·5	9·5	39·1	44·4
	National average	14·9	22·4	9·9	17·3	41·6	57·3

The point of this table is to show that there is really no consistent trend for both MHA classifications and all regions. Compare, for instance, Regions 6 and 8 (North East Thames and South West Thames). Region 6 used the Special Hospitals for both MHA classifications at about the national average for both five-year periods. Region 8 remained at about twice the national average for Mental Illness, but maintained a constant referral rate for Psychopathic Disorder, so that it did not reflect the 75 per cent increase in Table 4.1. Region 1 (Northern) increased its referral rate for both MHA classifications by something over double, but still remains below the national average for both categories, substantially so for Mental Illness. Region 11 (South-West) showed a substantial change in its admission rate of Psychopathic Disorder patients, but practically no change for Mental Illness.

Of course, these ratings represent a small number of patients. Each figure represents the number of patients admitted per million of the male population in a five-year period. In absolute terms, the largest group of patients are those in the Mental Illness category from the South West Thames Region. During 1961–5 there were thirty-two, or about eight a year. The Wessex admission rate represents an average of approximately two a year. For psychopathic patients, the numbers are, on average, somewhat smaller.

Is it possible to explain the observed changes in the referral rate for Special Hospital care in terms of changes in the patients or in the communities from which they come? I suggest that it would be very difficult to do so, although, of course, such changes may well be contributory. It seems altogether more likely that the alterations in admission rate are due to administrative changes, and that the administrative changes are the results of changes in attitudes and practices of the professionals who are responsible for looking after the patients.

Since 1970 the situation may have changed again. Published figures show a marked drop in the number of male admissions to Special Hospitals, from 285 in 1969 to 167 in 1977. Figures are not available for as detailed an analysis of this period as was possible for the 1960s, but the fall in admissions has occurred for both MHA diagnostic categories and geographical areas (Tables 4.4 and 4.5). Thus, it is unrealistic to suppose that there has been a change in attitude in, say, subnormality hospitals, since the fall has also occurred in patients classified as suffering from Mental Illness – who, by and large, are cared for in general psychiatric hospitals. Nor can one suppose that (for instance) one particular judge or psychiatrist has changed the policy in his area, for the drop in numbers is nationwide. The drop in numbers points to a change in policy of those who consider referrals from all referral sources and all areas – namely, in the Department of Health. It emphasises that admission rates may vary greatly simply as a result of administrative changes. Miller, Simons and Fein (1974) came to a similar explanation for variations in the proportion of informal admissions to National Health psychiatric hospitals. They wrote: 'our argument [is] that the particular regional policy, whether official or unofficial, is highly significant'. We should therefore look at the administrative process by which patients are admitted to a Special Hospital in order to identify whether there are key posts in the decision-making process which allow the holders of those posts to exert a strong influence on the referral rates.

Table 4.4 *Male Admissions for the Five-Year Period 1972–6 According to Diagnostic Category. (Figures made available by the Special Hospitals Research Unit.)*

MHA classification	1972	1973	1974	1975	1976
Mental Illness	132	106	103	96	99
Psychopathic Disorder	79	110	75	60	56
Subnormality	35	39	26	18	14
Severe Subnormality	17	14	7	4	7
Combination of above classifications	19	5	3	3	4
	282	274	214	181	180

The totals shown are not the same as those in the published figures. Thus, the total admissions for 1976 shown is 180, whereas the total in the published figures is 190. The difference arises from variations in the manner of recording, for instance, of a patient who is admitted on remand and returned after sentence.

Table 4.5 *Male Admissions for the Five-Year Period 1972–6 According to the Regional Health Authority areas. (Figures made available by the Special Hospitals Research Unit.)*

	1972	1973	1974	1975	1976	Totals
Northern	11	10	9	11	7	48
Yorks.	10	11	14	8	6	49
Trent	27	24	30	14	23	118
E. Anglia	7	5	3	4	2	21
N.W. Thames	22	26	17	14	14	93
N.E. Thames	13	16	17	16	14	75
S.E. Thames	19	17	19	13	12	80
S.W. Thames	17	18	13	8	7	63
Wessex	8	10	9	12	5	44
Oxford	15	16	7	9	6	53
S. West	14	10	15	6	13	58
W. Midlands	25	26	13	21	18	103
Mersey	17	24	6	8	9	54
N. West	12	11	11	8	6	48
Wales	10	12	9	4	13	38

The areas of the pre-1974 Regional Hospital Boards are not identical to those of the post-1974 Regional Health Authorities, but are near enough for present purposes. Information was lacking for 158 patients.

The management of the Special Hospitals in England and Wales is under the direct control of the Department of Health and Social Security, which is also responsible for deciding who shall be admitted to them. A doctor who feels that one of his patients should be considered for a Special Hospital place will make a formal request to the Department of Health and Social Security who will then evaluate the case on its merits and make a decision. When arriving at this decision, DHSS may or may not invite a member of the consultant staff of one of the Special Hospitals to examine the patient and evaluate the circumstances which have led to the request for Special Hospital care. Since indeterminate detention in a hospital requires the signature of two psychiatrists it is sensible that one of those signatures should be from a doctor who will assume medical responsibility for the patient in the event of his being detained. Otherwise there remains the possibility, as very occasionally happens, that a patient is detained on the authority of two psychiatrists, but cared for by a third psychiatrist, who may not feel that the detention is appropriate. Civil patients who are transferred from an NHS psychiatric hospital to a Special Hospital will have already been examined by two psychiatrists who will both have agreed that the patient ought to be detained in the NHS hospital, but for offender patients who may be transferred to the Special Hospital the case may be slightly different. First, they will almost always have been remanded in custody because of the seriousness of their offences, so that their medical care is the responsibility of the prison doctor, who will usually be the first signatory to the appropriate medical authorisation for compulsory detention. It is then common sense to arrange for a Special Hospital doctor to examine the patient and also for him to be the second signatory if he agrees with his prison-based colleague that Special Hospital treatment is appropriate. The prison medical officer will then make the formal application to DHSS for Special Hospital placement and his application will be supported by a Special Hospital doctor, on the basis of his own personal assessment of the patient. Under such circumstances, the Department can hardly refuse to accept the patient, since admission has been recommended by their own expert in that particular field.

In practice, the number of remand establishments within the penal system in England and Wales in which potential Special Hospital patients are likely to be found is very small. Yet these few establishments provided in the 1960s about half of the Special Hospital clientele (see Table 4.2). These establishments were producing some three patients per week, on average, who were subsequently admitted to a Special Hospital. Under such circumstances, it was inevitable that personal relationships built up between the few prison medical officers at the relevant remand establishments and the small number of Special Hospital psychiatrists. Consequently, the prison medical officers soon discovered what sort of patient Special Hospital consultants regarded as suitable for the facilities at their disposal, and it was the prison medical officers who made the initial decision that, in any given case, it might be appropriate to recommend to the court that a psychiatric disposal would be more appropriate than a normal penal one. Of course, if a prison medical officer did not recommend medical disposal but the offender's legal adviser felt that a medical disposal would be worth consideration, those advisers might have had the opportunity to arrange such psychiatric assessment as they wished. But it seems to be rare for a medical disposal to be organised against the recommendation of the prison medical officer. The reasons for this are speculative, but may well have to do with the relative inability of these patients to organise the legal system to their benefit. Consider, for instance, Rushing's status resource hypothesis, 'that individuals with more resources are better able to control their fates and hence resist legal coercion that would lead to hospitalisation'. It may also be that few solicitors come across many of these patients during a professional lifetime. This means that they have little experience of such cases, which in turn makes it less likely that they would suggest an outside medical opinion when a prison doctor has already indicated that medical disposal would be inappropriate.

It appears, therefore, that during the 1960s, in the case of England and Wales, the prison medical officers stood in a crucial position in the decision-making process, for it was their attitude, both personal and professional, which decided whether a prisoner was to be considered for a Special Hospital at all. They might think that the Special Hospital placement was a good idea and subsequently find that the Special Hospital consultant did not agree with them; but if the prison doctors did not suggest a Special Hospital placement in the first place, then no one else, in practice, had an opportunity to do so.

Recent studies show that the number of patients admitted to Special Hospitals fell during the 1970s. The fall is too large to be attributable to any fall in the general incidence of those conditions with which the Special Hospitals deal. It must be due to changes in the administrative procedures by which the patients are selected for Special Hospital care.

Public Attitudes and Special Hospital Admission

Finally, it is appropriate to consider whether a number of other general questions are involved in the way in which decisions are made about admitting patients to Special Hospitals. For instance, if the public begins to tolerate an increased level of violence in the community, then the greater tolerance is likely to be reflected in National Health Service psychiatric hospitals. This, in turn, reduces the demand for Special Hospital care for potentially dangerous or violent individuals. The corollary would be that those patients then admitted to a Special Hospital would be more violent than those who go there currently.

Secondly, demand for a Special Hospital is likely to be affected by the resources available in the alternative sources of residential care which, in practice, are the psychiatric or mental handicap hospitals. If the latter institutions decline to accept patients on transfer from the Special Hospitals, then either the Special Hospitals must expand, or they must cut down their intakes. The difficulties in arranging for a patient to be transferred out of a Special Hospital have recently been documented by Dell (1980), who emphasised, in particular, the long period which many patients have to endure after they have been considered by their responsible medical officers as suitable for transfer from a Special Hospital to an NHS psychiatric or (more usually) mental handicap hospital.

In November 1980 the Report of the Review of Rampton Hospital quoted a figure of 122 patients who need not be in Rampton. This raises a third question, namely, what is meant by a statement such as 'patient X need not be here'? Probably every hospital in the country has a substantial number of inmates who 'need not be there', which presumably means that they are not in need of the full resources which the hospital can offer. On the other hand, if they were not 'there' they would have to be somewhere else, and if the somewhere else does not exist, then they have no option other than to be 'there'. Dell hints at this when she points out that mental handicap consultants may well feel that they should allocate a vacant bed to a patient who is creating great difficulties to several members of his family by remaining at home, rather than to a patient who is already being cared for in hospital, albeit in the unnecessarily restricted circumstances of a Special Hospital. This brings in the wider issue of the resources which society is able and willing to allocate to any particularly difficult individual, at any given time. Reverting to those 122 patients referred to in the Rampton Report, it may be pointed out that they represent about 13 per cent of patients in Rampton at the present time (using Dell's figure of 883 as the patient population of Rampton in 1978). If the situation described by Dell became worse, so that fewer and fewer patients left the hospital, the proportion of those who 'need not be there' would grow and grow. Under such circumstances, it would be no more true to say that the patients 'need not be there' than that Rampton should recognise that its role would have changed, and it would have become, by degrees, another mental handicap hospital.

Perhaps with 13 per cent, or more, of patients who 'need not be there' the hospital should already be acknowledging that its role has changed. Coupled with this is the question of what people mean by the phrase 'he need not be in hospital'. The phrase presumably implies some notion of what a hospital is for, and that, once that function has been exercised, the need for it no longer exists. This is particularly the case where the hospital function is successfully exercised and the patient is cured. But what is a hospital 'for' when it has done all it can, and the patients remain more or less unchanged? Here, it seems to me, we could usefully bring back the word 'asylum' with the connotation that the place is designed to look after these people rather than to do to them such things as would make them more likely to survive in the community 'outside the hospital'. The change of name would lead to a change in expectation, for doctors would be offering asylum instead of admitting to hospital.

Which in a way brings us back to John Stuart Mill and deciding what we are trying to do. It has become almost an article of faith that living out of hospital is better than living in one. This has the corollary that patients should be 'treated' so as to help them make the change from hospital to non-hospital life, even when they appear to be reasonably content in hospital. Presumably, a utilitarian view would be to approach the matter purely on economic or cost-effective grounds. If a patient is willing to stay in hospital indefinitely, and it is cheaper for the community for him to do so, then there would be little point in seeking to change the situation. However, the current social philosophy seems to be that patients should be encouraged to 'better' themselves, and it may well be that many of us, as practitioners, are deeply affected by current philosophical views without normally being aware of it.

We recognise the logic of Mill's position and the need to protect the public. But, as doctors brought up in the Western tradition, we are taught the value of the individual and a medical obligation to the individual patient. The two objectives must frequently conflict. No wonder this is such an embarrassing subject for doctors.

Note

The author is pleased to acknowledge assistance provided by Mrs Elizabeth Parker of the Special Hospitals Research Unit, DHSS.

Part Two

Appraisals of Some Current Methods in the Assessment and Treatment of the Dangerous Offender

5 Psychometrics and Personality Theory in Relation to Dangerousness

RONALD BLACKBURN

During the past decade, it has become apparent that neither clinicians nor behavioural scientists have demonstrated the ability to distinguish clearly between those who are likely to exhibit dangerous behaviour and those who are not. The evidence to date indicates that there is no empirical support for any claims on the part of psychiatrists to forecast future dangerousness (Rubin, 1972; Steadman, 1973; Klein, 1976), and it has been contended that clinical judgements of dangerousness are 'less accurate than the flip of a coin' (Ennis and Litwack, 1974). This appears to be no less true of statistical predictions based on clinical, demographic, or life history variables (Wenk, Robinson and Smith, 1972; Hedlund, Sletten, Altman and Evenson, 1973).

In some of the prediction studies reported, psychological tests have been used either as sources of clinical judgement (Kozol, Boucher and Garofalo, 1972), or as quantitative predictors to be entered into actuarial equations (Wenk et al., 1972). Although there do not appear to be any data bearing directly on the predictive validity of such tests, the outcome of these studies suggests that they made little contribution. Postdictive studies of relationships of personality tests to violence, which form the bulk of research in this area, have not uncovered correlations of sufficient magnitude to warrant routine application (Megargee, 1970), nor have predictive studies of recidivism revealed very substantial or consistent relationships between personality variables and re-offending in general (Gough, Wenk and Rozynko, 1965). It would seem to be the case that the best predictor of future antisocial behaviour is past behaviour (Gough et al., 1965; Black, 1977). Even here, 'best' is relative. Wenk et al. (1972), for example, found that there was a nineteen to one chance against an offender with a violent admission offence committing a similar offence while on parole, and an eight to one chance against a violent parolee having been admitted to prison following a violent crime.

Against this discouraging background, it is not surprising that some have suggested that the prediction of dangerousness is an impossible task. They may well be right. However, at our present stage of knowledge this seems a premature conclusion. As long as we remain relatively ignorant of the psychological precursors of antisocial behaviour, what we put into our predictors amounts to no more than guess-work, or 'shotgun empiricism'.

This applies no less to the informal decision rules in clinical judgement than to the predictors entering into a multiple regression equation. Moreover, some of the failures in prediction may be more a reflection of the vagueness of the criteria we try to predict than a lack of predictive ability. Terms such as recidivism, parole violation, re-offending, or dangerous crime do not, after all, describe precise or homogeneous classes of behaviour.

In this chapter, dangerous crime refers to violent crime involving the likelihood of physical injury to the victim, and as synonymous with anti-social aggression. There are problems with such a definition, as with the definition of aggression itself (Zillman, 1979), particularly since, from a psychological viewpoint, the motivation of an aggressive act is as important as its consequences for the victim. Nevertheless, it serves to focus attention on crimes whose harmfulness to society would not be disputed. The contribution of the person to violence is explored, and some studies of mentally abnormal offenders are described in an attempt to evaluate the potential utility of personality variables in the prediction of dangerousness. First, however, it is pertinent to consider the nature of the difficulty in predicting dangerous behaviour.

The Prediction Problem

Monahan (1976) has summarised seven large-scale studies of attempts to identify which of those released from American prisons, or from institutions for mentally abnormal offenders, would commit violent crimes, and notes that between 54 and 99 per cent of those predicted to be dangerous did not in fact subsequently commit such crimes. This high false positive rate is amply illustrated by the effects of judicial decisions in the United States to release large numbers of mentally abnormal offenders detained for long periods in maximum security hospitals as supposedly dangerous. As a result of the Baxstrom case in New York State (Hunt and Wiley, 1968; Steadman and Cocozza, 1974), and similar decisions in Massachusetts (McGarry and Parker, 1974), and in Pennsylvania (Monahan, 1976), substantial numbers of abnormal offenders have been transferred to civil hospitals or to the community. Follow-up studies have consistently indicated a very low rate of subsequent violence. These 'experiments' may to some extent underestimate the potential dangerousness of the populations of such institutions, since those transferred were relatively old and long-term patients, and in all cases those who did re-offend tended to be younger. Nevertheless, the lesson would seem to be that dangerousness is considerably overestimated.

The focus on overprediction, however, reflects a social rather than a scientific concern. Few would wish to argue with the view that if the prevention of future dangerousness involves detaining two or more harmless individuals for every dangerous offender, the game may not be worth the candle. Nevertheless, in statistical terms, the goal of prediction is not only to minimise false positives, but also false negatives. Although all studies reported to date yield high false positive rates, and have an overall accuracy which is typically less than that which would have resulted from calling all subjects 'non-dangerous', there is some evidence that considerable reduction in false negatives can be achieved. Cocozza and Steadman (1974), for example, derived a Legal Dangerousness Scale from the past criminal records of Baxstrom patients, and this yielded an impressive ratio of true positives to false negatives of almost 4 : 1. But even though the scale correctly identified the majority of those released into the community who became dangerous, it nevertheless produced a false positive rate of 69 per cent, and an overall error rate of 28 per cent, in contrast to the 14 per cent error which would have resulted from a blanket prediction of 'non-dangerous'.

The point is that dangerousness predictions may have some degree of validity, but not sufficient to improve on prediction from the base rate alone. In fact, the improvement in detecting true positives in the preceding study was achieved with a predictor which accounted for only 4 per cent of the variance in re-offending ($r = 0.201$, $p < 0.01$). Another investigation illustrates the influence of the base rate on this kind of prediction. Working within the framework of a theoretical model relating undersocialised behaviour to slow formation of conditioned responses, Tong (1959) measured speed of autonomic conditioning in institutionalised mentally abnormal offenders. The relapse rate of slow conditioners one year after release from the institution was subsequently found to be significantly higher than that of fast conditioners. Not only did conditioning score correctly identify 95 per cent of those who relapsed, it yielded a false positive rate of 47 per cent, which is lower than that commonly found in prediction studies. The base rate of relapse in the sample of forty-five patients was 42 per cent, but the accuracy rate of prediction from conditioning score alone was 62 per cent. In this study, then, an objective predictor was able to 'beat' the base rate, and reduce both false negatives and false positives.

Successful prediction, in this case, was not due to high 'validity' of the predictor, which is quite modest ($\phi = 0.38$, calculated from Tong's data). Rather does it reflect the fact that, contrary to what many psychologists appear to believe, small validity coefficients can result in useful prediction, provided that the base rate is close to 50 per cent (Curtis, 1971). However, relapse in this study referred to any deviant behaviour resulting in further institutionalisation, and not simply dangerous behaviour. The base rate of further violence in patients released from this kind of institution is probably about 10 per cent (Black, 1977). At this level, a predictor would have to correlate with the criterion to the extent of 0.7 to yield even trivial improvement over a blanket prediction of 'non-dangerous' (see Curtis, 1971). As validity coefficients of psychological measures (as well as clinical judgement, Goldberg, 1968), are only rarely greater than 0.4, there would seem to be some justification for the pessimism of those who feel that the base rate problem presents an insurmountable barrier in dangerousness predictions.

A related issue concerns the frequently encountered assertion that over-lapping score distributions between groups, who are significantly differentiated by a variable, render that variable useless for individual prediction. This is not so. There is in effect no difference between making statements about differences in group behaviour and statements about the likely behaviour of members of the group. Clinical prediction is always probabilistic, never absolute. To take an example, Mack (1969) found that a rating scale of Antisocial Aggression significantly differentiated between recidivists and non-recidivists (biserial $r = 0.55$), but concluded incorrectly that the scale would not allow valid prediction of parole violation in the individual case. As the base rate appears to be close to 50 per cent in this instance, and assuming normal score distributions, it should in fact be possible to derive a cutting score such that prediction of recidivism for *any* high scorer and of non-recidivism for a low scorer would result in some 67 per cent correct decisions. A validity coefficient of this magnitude would yield better than chance prediction even with a base rate of 20 per cent (Curtis, 1971).

The Contribution of the Person to Violence

Clinical evaluations of dangerousness are by their nature person-oriented. Although in practice the question sometimes arises as to whether a patient is dangerous to a particular individual, such as a child at risk for 'battering', or the target of a delusional system, more commonly clinicians attempt to decide whether a person is dangerous *in general*. An obvious reason for this is that we are not usually in a position to predict what thwarting or threatening situations a person will encounter at some future date. In this respect, the situation inevitably imposes an upper limit on what we can predict. The traditional assumption has been that reliable assessment of how easily a person becomes angry, or how frequently he displays aggressive behaviour, should permit predictive statements about the likelihood of future violence. This is implicit in the concept of dangerousness, since dangerousness is an attribute of the person. The reason why society entrusts decisions about dangerousness to mental health professionals is the belief that dangerous acts reflect 'inner' peculiarities or deviant tendencies which the clinician should be able to detect, a belief, it may be noted, which has been fostered by psychiatry's espousal of the psychic determinism of psychoanalysis and by the prevalent 'illness' model of psychological abnormality.

One consequence is that most procedures developed for the assessment of aggression in a clinical context are global trait measures derived from a sampling of self-reported tendencies or reactions to projective tests. Megargee and Menzies (1971), for example, reviewed over thirty situational, inventory, projective and adjective check-list techniques for assessing aggression. Apart from check-lists, which tend to focus on temporary mood states of anger, all represented attempts to measure hostile or aggressive dispositions.

The notion that individuals carry around with them stable tendencies which will manifest themselves with some degree of consistency in different situations has, however, been a major source of controversy in recent years. This controversy was orchestrated by Mischel (1968), who after reviewing attempts to predict behaviour from psychometrically determined traits or psychodynamic inferences about states and traits, concluded that 'With the possible exception of intelligence, highly generalised behavioural consistencies have not been demonstrated, and the concept of personality traits as broad response dispositions is thus untenable' (Mischel, 1968, p. 146). He further argued that indices of relevant past behaviour provide the best predictions of future behaviour, including antisocial behaviour, and that these are superior to 'complex inferences about underlying states and traits'.

While those enamoured of Skinnerian environmental determinism have seized on these conclusions as support for the view that behaviour is largely a function of the situation, Mischel (1973, 1977) has been at pains to repudiate a 'situationist' position. As he points out, it is meaningless to argue that it is the person rather than the situation, or vice versa, which is *the* primary determinant of behaviour, since the contribution of individual differences is likely to vary for different situations. For example, differences between people in aggressive behaviour may be apparent at a political rally, but not during a lecture on anatomy. It may also be noted at this point that the fact that situations exert considerable effects on behaviour has little bearing on the question of generalised behaviour consistencies. All that a trait concept implies is that individuals will tend to retain their relative rank order on some variable despite changes in the situation. The issue, as Mischel and others see it, is that the contribution of the person is specific for particular situations, and that behaviour does not show the appreciable consistency across different situations implied by trait concepts. Mischel's approach, then, is one variant of the interactionist position (Endler and Magnusson, 1976).

Now this position is obviously of considerable relevance to the question of how far we can predict dangerousness. If behaviour is indeed relatively specific to situations, then we are wasting our time trying to determine the 'hostility' or 'aggressiveness' of potentially dangerous individuals, since such broad dispositions are, in these terms, probably little more than semantic fictions. Shah (1978) has recently implied as much. As he puts it, 'efforts to understand, assess, predict, prevent, and change dangerous behaviours must consider the effects of setting and situational factors as well as the interactions between these and the characteristics of the person' (p. 227). In a similar vein, Clarke (1977) has proposed that the psychology of crime should focus on the immediate circumstances surrounding a criminal act, and that the relevant person variables to consider are those which vary with such circumstances, whether life events, crises, or perceptions of opportunities.

These arguments are highly persuasive. Not only do they highlight the shortcomings of our traditional assessments, they lead to a realistic focus on reducing the opportunities for antisocial behaviour (see also Monahan, 1976). However, if they are correct, they imply that we should abandon attempts to forecast future dangerousness. If behaviour depends largely on person–situation interactions, then in the absence of information about relevant situations, we cannot know in advance which person variables are to be evaluated. Indeed, it is tempting to conclude that this is precisely the reason why neither clinical nor actuarial attempts to predict dangerousness have met with any notable success.

There is, however, good reason to question Mischel's conclusion that aggressive behaviour is situationally inconsistent. Olweus (1979) has recently reviewed the evidence on the longitudinal stability of aggression as measured by ratings, peer nominations and direct observations, periods covered by the studies ranging from six months to twenty-one years. Over twelve investigations, the average correlation between behaviour samples for the two occasions of assessment, after corrections for measurement error, was 0·79. Given the time spans involved, it is difficult to account for this degree of consistency in terms of constant situations, and the conclusion that there are generalised personal attributes which account for this regularity seems inescapable.

Although Olweus was not specifically concerned with aggressive criminal behaviour, one of the studies included in his review provides evidence on this issue. In the Cambridge Study on Delinquent Development (Farrington, 1978) 411 boys were examined intensively between the ages of 8 and 22. Aggressiveness was assessed by means of teacher ratings in the early years, and from interview reports of fights and the use of weapons in the later adolescent stages. Of about a quarter of the boys who later became delinquent, twenty-seven were identified as violent delinquents by the age of 21, and members of this group were also more likely to be recidivists. The stability of aggressive behaviour was indicated not only by significant relationships between teacher ratings made at different stages during the early years, but also by significant associations between rated aggressiveness at ages 8 to 10 and self-reported aggressive tendencies between ages 16 and 18. Of the violent delinquents, nearly half had been identified as aggressive at the 8 to 10 year old stage, while teacher ratings of 12 year olds placed 70 per cent of the subsequently violent delinquents, 49 per cent of the non-violent delinquents and 23 per cent of the non-delinquents in the most aggressive category. Thus, although not all of those observed to be aggressive prepubertally became violent delinquents, the majority of those who did were identified as aggressive early in life. Turpin, Mahar and Smith (1973) and Hare (1980) have also found that an early history of fighting, as well as other childhood behaviour disorders such as hyperactivity, enuresis and temper tantrums, significantly differentiates habitually aggressive adult offenders.

Some further evidence on the stability of aggressive behaviour is provided by a recent study of the institutional behaviour of mentally abnormal offenders (Blackburn and Lee-Evans, in preparation). Ratings of ward behaviour were made by nursing staff on sixty-three patients newly admitted to a maximum security hospital. Factor analysis identified two major factors, one of which reflected aggressive and nonconforming behaviour and was labelled Psychopathy (PY: Blackburn, 1979). Ratings were obtained two years later for forty-two of the patients remaining in the hospital, the assessments being made in different wards by different staff. The correlation between PY scores at the time of admission and those obtained two years later was 0·77 ($p < 0.001$). After correction for rater unreliability, this coefficient actually becomes unity, indicating that these patients retained their rank order in aggressiveness to a very marked degree. It is worth noting that an earlier study in the same institution (Davis, 1974) revealed a correlation of 0·58 between a similar rating scale of aggressiveness and frequency of aggressive episodes recorded over a two-month period following the rating. The ratings therefore are related to overt behaviour, and are not simply a function of staff stereotypes.

It is, then, entirely appropriate to talk of a stable and generalised disposition of aggressiveness, and this is an attribute which appears to characterise violent offenders. Indeed, the finding that previous antisocial behaviour is the best predictor of future violence (Wenk *et al.*, 1972; Black, 1977) amounts to prima facie evidence for such a disposition. The question of the 'existence' of such a trait does not therefore seem to be in doubt.

Dispositions and Specific Events

The preceding discussion was concerned with the relationship between *samples* of behaviour at different points in time, and the evidence indicates that average behaviour at one period predicts average behaviour at a later period to an appreciable degree. In other words, knowledge of a person's standing on a trait measure of aggressiveness should enable us to predict the extent to which he will show such behaviour over situations *in the aggregate*. This summary, or average, nature of trait concepts appears to have been a source of confusion in much of the 'person–situation' debate. Mischel (1973, 1977), for example, sees it as appropriate to regard traits as summary abstractions of behaviour, but he goes on to demand that dispositions must pass the test of predicting behaviour 'in specific situations' if their utility is to be justified.

However, the requirement that dispositional terms predict specific behaviours is unreasonable, because this is not the job they were designed to do. Moreover, it is doubtful whether Mischel's own cognitive person variables do it either. If by 'behaviour in a specific situation' Mischel means a *unique* event, then no prediction is possible, since by definition a unique event happens only once. This is, in fact, the classic dilemma of the idiographic approach which Mischel advocates, namely, that to make any generalisations about an event, one must repudiate its uniqueness. But he does not apparently mean unique in the sense of unrepeatable. By specific situations he appears to mean such situations as 'school' or 'home', and not, for example, classroom A in the presence of teacher B at time C. As he states, 'obviously behaviour is not entirely situation specific; we do not have to relearn everything in every new situation' (1973, p. 261). Similarly, the person variables he proposes, such as outcome expectancies or incentive preferences, are to be construed as '*relatively* specific' (1973, p. 272, italics mine).

But once this is acknowledged, we are into the realm of dispositional statements. Dispositional description in terms of traits derives ultimately from the raw data of the single event, but represents generalisation over an aggregate of such events. It predicts the single event only to the extent that the latter shares commonality with other events. But Mischel's own person variables also have this dispositional quality (Alston, 1975). In this respect, they differ from conventional trait constructs only in being less generalised. That they are more contextually bound does not alter the fact that they none the less predict behaviour in the aggregate, and not 'specific' behaviour.

Now, as Alston (1975) has noted, if the only objection to trait concepts was their overgenerality, the obvious remedy would be to transform them into more specific dispositions. It does not, in fact, seem unreasonable to argue that by assessing the *kinds* of response a person exhibits in particular *classes* of situation we may enhance prediction. This is precisely the interactionist solution (Endler and Magnusson, 1976), but it should be apparent that this does not reflect a radical departure from trait measurement. It is simply a more specific form of dispositional description.

We have recently begun to explore this approach in assessing the aggressiveness of mentally abnormal offenders (Blackburn and Lee-Evans, in preparation). An S-R Inventory of Hostility (Endler and Hunt, 1968) was constructed, and this required the subject to indicate the intensity of each of twelve modes of response (for example, 'swear', 'feel angry', 'want to hit someone') to fourteen situations involving annoying or thwarting situations (for example, 'you have been blamed for something you didn't do', 'someone threatens to beat you up'). Factor analysis indicated that response modes cluster into three categories of overt aggression, anger arousal, and autonomic arousal. Situations also fall into three clusters relating to insult, frustration, and harm. However, both the response factors and the situation factors are oblique, and there is clearly a strong general factor pervading all responses and all situation classes. This can be described as a general disposition of aggressiveness, and a trait questionnaire measuring this dimension in fact correlates with all response and situation factors to the extent of 0.5 to 0.6. We have as yet not obtained data relating these measures to behaviour in particular classes of situation, but similar measures identifying responses to classes of anxiety-arousing situation have been shown to be good predictors of response in particular settings (Goldfried and Kent, 1972). However, the main point for present purposes is that these more specific dispositions are not independent of each other and are themselves predictable to a significant degree from the generalised disposition measure. Whether improved prediction of violence results from the more specific measures remains to be seen.

The degree of generalisation in broad dispositional measures, then, may not be as serious a problem as has been supposed. A more significant factor may be their explanatory status. Alston (1975) has drawn attention to an important distinction between personality constructs and suggests that there are two kinds of construct employed in personality theory. The first refers to stimulus–response regularities in behaviour, and is represented by response dispositions, such as aggressiveness (T constructs). The second refers to purposive and latent variables such as needs, values, or expectancies (P-C constructs). T constructs are probabilistic and represent dispositional statements of the 'if-then' kind. They explain behaviour only in so far as they *imply* something responsible for regularity. P-C constructs, on the other hand, are hypothetical motivational variables and serve the purpose of causal explanation. One implication of this analysis is that T constructs and P-C constructs are not incompatible. It would, for example, be quite feasible to account for dispositional regularity of aggressive behaviour in terms of tendency to appraise certain kinds of situation as threatening, or as a consequence of expectations of reinforcing outcomes for assaultive behaviours. Mischel's person variables, it will be noted, are clearly (relatively) specific P-C constructs.

The point about T constructs, however, is their probabilistic nature, and given that we do not anticipate that a highly aggressive person, for example, will behave aggressively on all possible occasions, such constructs cannot provide a *fundamental* account of behaviour. Reference to such constructs as mood state, competing needs, or outcome expectancies is necessary if behaviour is not invariant. T constructs are hence only a first stab at describing a person.

The Measurement of Aggressiveness

There is currently debate about the role of unlearned factors in anger arousal, and it has been suggested that there may be primitive connections between anger and aggressive behaviour which become modified with early experience (Berkowitz, 1969). Nevertheless, there seems to be general consensus among behaviour theorists that aggressive behaviour is shaped largely through modelling and reinforcement. It should be clear from the preceding discussion that dispositional description of a person in terms of a trait of aggressiveness implies no necessary theoretical commitment, but it seems reasonable to assume that such a trait represents learned behaviour. Psychoanalytic instinct models still have their proponents, and this appears to be the reason for the continued use of projective tests such as the Rorschach in American forensic psychiatry (Kozol *et al.*, 1972; Revitch and Schlesinger, 1978). In the absence of any empirical support for an instinctual origin of human aggression (Zillman, 1979), the use of such devices seems questionable.

Given that a trait refers to aggregate behaviour, the most reliable determination of a disposition of aggressiveness would in principle entail extended observation of the frequency and intensity of injurious behaviours. In practice, of course, we must rely on behaviour samples of a more restricted and indirect kind, and self-report and observer rating scales offer the most convenient and commonly used samples. The use of the former will be considered here.

Megargee and Menzies (1971) reviewed a number of self-report measures of hostility and aggression, and concluded that at best only low-level relationships with external criteria had been established. A number of these were included in a factor analytic study of personality variables measured in mentally abnormal offenders (Blackburn, 1972), and it was found that over half the variance was accounted for by two factors. The first appeared to measure *angry aggression, that is, the tendency to react with anger and overt verbal or physical aggression, or what Zillman (1979) has termed 'annoyance-motivated'* aggression. The second seemed to be measuring *hostility*, that is, the tendency to evaluate others in negative or unfavourable terms. Scales were subsequently constructed to measure these two dimensions (Blackburn, 1974). In general, the Aggressiveness (*Ag*) scale has shown slightly stronger correlations with external criteria than has the Hostility (*Ho*) scale, although relationships are generally modest. The *Ag* scale correlated significantly with a rating of assaultiveness derived from the case notes of eighty patients at a maximum security hospital ($r = 0.37$, $p < 0.001$). Also, in Davis's study of the institutional adjustment of mentally abnormal offenders in a similar hospital (Davis, 1974), the scale correlated with staff ratings of aggressiveness ($r = 0.31$, $p < 0.05$), and with number of aggressive episodes over a two-month period ($r = 0.31$, $p < 0.05$). Edmunds and Kendrick (1980) have reported very similar findings in delinquent samples. They identified comparable factors of Aggressiveness and Hostility in inventory data, and obtained correlations of self-reported aggressiveness with staff ratings of 0.3.

A personality variable frequently linked with antisocial behaviour is impulsivity (for example, Gough *et al.*, 1965; Schalling, 1978), and a scale developed to measure this variable (*Im*: Blackburn, 1973) was found to show small correlations with history of assaultive crimes in mentally abnormal offenders ($r = 0.26$, $p < 0.05$), and with greater variety of crimes ($r = 0.30$, $p < 0.01$). It has also been found to discriminate recidivists from first offenders in American prisoners (Como, 1977). A recent study (Blackburn, 1979) indicates that *Im* and *Ag* define a broad factor dimension which also includes *Ho*, as well as scales of extraversion and psychopathic traits. This dimension has been labelled Psychopathy, and it correlates significantly with a corresponding staff rating scale ($r = 0.37$, $p < 0.01$). Of particular relevance to the prediction of dangerousness are the findings of Black (1977) that among discharged mentally abnormal offenders, *Im* significantly distinguishes those who re-offend in general, and those who commit further assaultive crimes in particular. However, as in other studies, record of previous convictions was found to be the best predictor of re-offending.

These correlations suggest that self-report scales of aggressiveness have some degree of validity, and as was indicated earlier, they might well have predictive utility under conditions in which the base rate for aggressive crimes was close to 50 per cent. However, the magnitude of the correlations suggests that their predictive utility is limited. It is this kind of validity coefficient which led Mischel (1968) to question the notion of broad dispositional regularities in behaviour, but for reasons discussed earlier, we must seek explanations in terms other than the 'nonexistence' of an aggressive disposition.

One obvious possibility is that self-reports are subject to falsification. However, this would not account for the positive correlations obtained, and Edmunds and Kendrick (1980) found little change in the correlation between self-reported and rated aggressiveness when Lie scale scores were partialled out. In fact, deliberate falsification (as opposed to distorted self-evaluation) is likely to arise only when situational pressures create strong motivation for favourable self-presentation, as for example when subjects are being considered for release from an institution. A more plausible reason is that the data samples on which self-report and observer measures are based are only partially overlapping. A self-report, for example, depends on the subject's perception of both covert and overt reactions over a wide range of life situations, whereas ratings draw on a more restricted sampling of behaviour (Becker, 1960). Olweus (1980) has recently discussed the sampling problems which are likely to attenuate validity coefficients of both self-report and rating measurements, and has shown that when samples of the elements of aggressive behaviour are matched (for example, the forms of response), cross-media correlations tend to be in the region of 0·5. He also points out that the question of reliability in criterion variables is often overlooked, and that this may substantially reduce validity coefficients. For the same reason, the validity of predictors of dangerousness may underestimate validity, and as Wenk *et al.* (1972) note, the incidence of reported dangerous crime may not be a reliable indicator of the actual occurrence of violent behaviour. Unfortunately, investigators in this area must work with the unreliable criterion.

Beyond the Univariate Prediction of Dangerousness

It was suggested earlier that one way of enhancing the predictive accuracy of dispositional measures might be to increase their specificity. It is probable, however, that there is an inherent limit on the validity of predicting the likelihood of aggression from a *single* trait measure. Apart from psychometric reasons for this, it seems unlikely that behaviour in any situation is a function of a single variable. Laboratory studies of aggressive behaviour have indicated that there are a number of person variables which can both facilitate and inhibit aggressive responding (Berkowitz, 1977). The arousal of anxiety, for example, has been shown to have an inhibitory effect, and Berkowitz notes that the usual facilitative effect of the availability of weapons may be reversed if weapons arouse anxiety.

Combining variables may therefore be a further way of improving predictive accuracy. Such an approach is exemplified in the application of multiple regression to prediction problems, but this fails to capture non-linear effects. It may be both more profitable and psychologically more meaningful to examine non-linear interactions between personality variables. Mischel (1973) notes the utility of the 'moderator variable' approach to prediction, although he regards it as reflecting 'the uniqueness of stimulus equivalences and response equivalences for each person'. As has been indicated above, we are not in the business of predicting 'unique' events, and the question of the utility of prediction from the interaction of generalised dispositional measures must be answered empirically.

An illustration of the potential utility of moderator variables in predicting aggression is to be found in the work of Olweus (1973). He proposed that in any account of aggressive behaviour the interaction of aggressive dispositions and habitual tendencies to inhibit such behaviour must be considered. Using a story completion test to measure aggressive and inhibitory tendencies in young adolescent boys, he predicted that where inhibition was weak, test measures of aggressiveness would correlate positively with overt aggression as assessed by peer ratings. Where inhibition was strong, test aggression should correlate negatively with observed aggression, since aroused aggressive tendencies would be blocked by higher inhibitions. The predicted relationships were confirmed, test aggression showing a correlation of +·62 with overt aggression in those with low inhibitions, but a correlation of −·55 in those with strong inhibitions. Inhibition therefore 'moderated' the relationship between aggressive tendencies and actual behaviour.

Inhibitions against aggression are also central to Megargee's concept of the 'overcontrolled' assaultive offender (Megargee, 1966). According to this model, 'undercontrolled' offenders are those with weak inhibitions and they are likely to behave aggressively with some regularity even in the face of minor provocation. Overcontrolled individuals, in contrast have very strong inhibitions, and will therefore aggress only when instigation (anger arousal) is sufficiently intense to overcome inhibitions. It is predicted that overcontrolled offenders will commit aggressive offences very rarely, but with extreme intensity when they do. Support for the hypothesis was obtained in a study of mentally abnormal offenders (Blackburn, 1968), in which it was found that those who had committed murder or attempted murder, as compared with less extreme assaultives, were significantly more controlled, inhibited and defensive on psychological tests, and significantly less likely to have a prior criminal record. In a later study of fifty-six murderers, almost half showed such characteristics (Blackburn, 1971). Megargee's hypothesis also received some partial experimental support from Taylor (1967), who found that overcontrolled subjects delivered less intense shocks than undercontrolled subjects in response to provocation. However, the lower arousal of the overcontrolled could simply mean that they were less annoyed by provocation. This highlights a difficulty with Megargee's model. It assumes that the intensity of aggression in the overcontrolled assaultive reflects an accumulation or summation of anger arousal to repeated provocation, an 'energy' model which is not in accord with current knowledge of aggression. Moreover, the model takes no account of aggressiveness as a disposition itself, the assumption being that an aggressive act is a function of temporary (or accumulated) anger arousal and the degree of inhibitory tendencies. Megargee's scale of Overcontrolled Hostility (OH) does not, in fact, permit us to separate aggressive 'habits' from inhibitory tendencies. In the writer's study of aggression scales (Blackburn, 1972), OH had a high negative loading on the factor of angry aggression, and hence it seems largely to measure a weak aggressive disposition. Although Megargee's hypothesis has undoubtedly helped to further our understanding of why unaggressive individuals occasionally commit extremely violent offences, it may be more appropriate to construe such acts as 'appraisal-mediated' (Zillman, 1979) rather than as impulsive reactions to intense or accumulated anger. The essential characteristic of overcontrolled offenders may be not so much that they inhibit aggression but rather that they have learned non-aggressive, avoidant ways of coping with annoyance (cf. Scarpetti, 1974), which are ineffective when provocation is perceived as ongoing. Such individuals would lack appropriate learned discriminations about when to terminate an aggressive sequence, and hence would be more likey to seriously injure the victim (Blackburn, 1971).

One advantage of identifying 'types' such as the overcontrolled assaultive offender is that it may assist in overcoming the base rate problem. The base rate of violence may be higher in some groups of offender and we may therefore be able to derive valid predictors more readily for these. The overcontrolled group, for example, appears to represent one for whom the base rate is low, and it is probable that in this case we will do no better than predicting 'no further violence'. The prognosis for murderers is, in fact, commonly regarded as good. For under-controlled or habitually aggressive offenders, on the other hand, the base rate for further violence is probably quite high, and it seems relevant in this context that those identified as having personality disorder or psycho-pathic personality seem significantly more likely to re-offend following release from maximum security hospitals (Quinsey, Warneford, Pruesse and Link, 1975; Black, 1977). Although contemporary personality theorists prefer description in terms of dimensions rather than discrete types, empirical determination of how people vary in *patterns* of dimensions provides a basis for identifying naturally occurring 'moderators'.

The writer's study of homicides (Blackburn, 1971) yielded four groups distinguished by different combinations of personality variables, and these same types have been found to recur as the major categories in 'normal' homicides (McGurk, 1978), American female prisoners (Widom, 1978), English male prisoners (McGurk and McGurk, 1979) and offenders categorised as personality disorders (Blackburn, 1975). They therefore seem to represent the main personality types occurring among offenders more generally. It has become apparent that these four 'types' are formed from combinations of two dimensions of Psychopathy (PY) and Social Withdrawal (SW: Blackburn, 1979). Thus high scorers on PY can be divided into a socially outgoing group (primary psychopaths) and a with-drawn, anxious group (secondary psychopaths), while low scorers on PY also fall into sociable and withdrawn sub-groups. In a series of studies of offenders it has been found that SW acts as a moderator variable in the relationship of PY with psychological variables. Few differences have been found between the two groups scoring low on PY, but among high PY scorers, those scoring high on SW, that is, secondary psychopaths, differ significantly from primary psychopaths in being less aroused physio-logically, less able to produce vivid imagery, and more likely to receive high ratings on Cleckley's criteria of psychopathy (Blackburn, 1980).

The moderator effect of the Social Withdrawal factor can also be seen when criminal records are examined. Combining the data from three studies in which these types were identified (Blackburn, 1971, 1975; Black-burn and Lee-Evans, in preparation), a total of 148 mentally abnormal offenders being involved, it is found that the following percentages show a history of two or more aggressive crimes, that is, may be regarded as habitually violent offenders: high PY – high SW, 20 per cent; high PY – low SW, 53 per cent; low PY – high SW, 8 per cent; low PY – low SW, 30 per cent. These differences are very significant ($\chi^2 = 16.52$, $d.f. = 3$, $p < 0.001$), and it is apparent that there is an additive effect of psychopathy and sociability, those who are non-psychopathic and withdrawn being least likely to be violent, those who are psychopathic and sociable being the most likely. On the other hand when history of sexual offences is examined, the respective percentages for the four groups are 41, 22, 42 and 17 per cent ($\chi^2 = 8\cdot96$, $d.f. = 3$, $p < 0\cdot05$). In this case, then, PY exerts little influence, those scoring highly on SW being more likely to have a history of sexual offences (see also Howells and Wright, 1978). However, further examination is necessary to determine whether there are differences in the distribution of aggressive and non-injurious sexual crimes.

Heilbrun (1979) has recently indicated that intelligence may moderate the relationship between psychopathy and violent crime. Using an inventory criterion of the psychopathy dimension, he found that 90 per cent of prisoners who were psychopathic and below average in intelligence had been admitted to prison following conviction for a violent crime. For psychopaths who were above average in intelligence, the percentage convicted of a violent crime did not differ from the 58 per cent among non-psychopaths. Unfortunately, this study examined only the pre-admission crime. In this kind of research it would seem important to assess the frequency of violence.

These data, then, indicate that classifying offenders by means of personality variables can produce discriminations among those who have behaved dangerously in the past. It remains to be seen whether such a classification predicts future violence.

Conclusions

It has been argued in this chapter that the degree of consistency in aggressive behaviour has been underestimated in recent discussions of personality, and that dispositional measures of aggression may to this extent be able to identify those who are more likely to commit violent crimes. This is not to suggest that aggressive tendencies are rigidly fixed or unmodifiable, nor does it imply any undue optimism in our ability to forecast the commission of violent crimes in the future. Quite apart from the element of arbitrariness inherent in identifying the occurrence of dangerous crimes, it is apparent that many of them occur in response to temporary pressures, under the influence of temporary mood or alcohol-induced states, or are contextually bound. On the other hand, people tend to create their environments, and many crimes of violence are apparently typical of the offender. What is typical is predictable.

Finally, it must be emphasised that there is no such thing as 'trait theory'. To say that a person has strong aggressive tendencies is to say no more than that under conditions of threat or annoyance there is a high probability that he will exhibit injurious behaviour. Confidence in our probability statements will only be assured when we have developed better dispositional measures than those currently available, and when we have a clearer idea of what attributes of the person are responsible for those tendencies.

6 Assessment and Treatment of Dangerous Sexual Offenders

DEREK PERKINS

This chapter will review evidence on the assessment and treatment of sexual offenders and in particular, those offenders who might, for reasons of the persistence or harmfulness of their behaviour, be regarded as dangerous.

Assessment

Cultural and Social Perspectives

Is it possible to recognise and treat the dangerous sexual offender? Within this seemingly straightforward question lie many of the assumptions and problems which have arisen in other areas of psychological and criminological research. At the heart of the matter is the question of how far it is possible to predict and manipulate behaviour by reference to factors supposedly residing within the individual: 'personality', 'attitudes', 'drives', and so on. Mischel's (1968) review of traditional personality research concluded that, with the exception of intelligence, correlations between measurements of personality characteristics and observable behaviours usually amounted to something less than 0·3, that is, accounting for less than 10 per cent of total behavioural variance. Mischel (1969) advocated a 'social behavioural' approach to personality, focusing on the functional relationships between a person's behaviour and the circumstances of his life.

What then of sexual offending and, more particularly, dangerous sexual offending? Might it be that assessments of an individual offender in one situation at one point in time will predict the occurrence and nature of subsequent sexual offending? If so, assessment and treatment are meaningful concepts. If, however, as in the case of most 'personality traits', situational factors are of primary importance, then the prediction and control of dangerous sexual offending will rest most heavily on considerations of the offender's, and the victim's physical, social and cultural environments.

Hinton (1978) points out the limitations of criminological investigations restricted to one level of analysis (for example, psychophysiological, psychological, or sociological). Nowhere is this more germane than in the field of sexual offending. Amir (1971) and Curtis (1974), amongst others, have illustrated the influence of cultural and sub-cultural values in bringing about the situations in which sexual offences occur and in shaping the attitudes and behaviour of those involved, victims, offenders, police and the judiciary.

Howells (1979a and 1981a) has demonstrated that there is a significant discrepancy between the public's view of, and the facts of pedophilia. The relationship between the pedophile and his victim is usually based on feelings of affection. The pedophile is often attracted to the child's passivity and innocence rather than simply his or her sexual characteristics. Contrasted with these findings is the public's tendency to over-emphasise the pedophile's dangerousness and degree of mental disturbance.

Purposes of Assessment

In the context of sexual offending, the assessment of individual offenders may have a variety of purposes, amongst these being predictions of future offending, decisions about release from custody, judgements about treatment suitability and evaluations of therapeutic outcome. Whether or not stated explicitly, any form of assessment carries with it implications for intervention, that is, some course of action which will impinge upon the offender. A central issue in assessment, therefore, is whether the offender welcomes or opposes the implied intervention. Whilst the actual methods of assessment may be similar in, for example, assessing for release an offender serving an indeterminate sentence and assessing a volunteer offender for treatment suitability, the two offenders in question will clearly construe their situations differently. This may have a direct bearing on the outcome of the assessments and the levels of confidence which can be attached to them.

In the case of assessment for early release, the offender, correctly or incorrectly, will often sense considerable pressure on him to co-operate if he desires release from custody. Offenders appearing before the courts are under a similar pressure to co-operate in assessment procedures in which they might not otherwise have chosen to take part. Whether such pressure is ethically acceptable is, of course, a moral judgement. It rests primarily upon considerations of the potential harm to future victims and the rights of the offender; whether he is able to give informed consent and the unpleasant and intrusiveness of the procedures to be used are two important elements.

Broad-Based Assessment

Barlow (1976) points to the need for examination of three areas of an offender's functioning: sexual arousal, socio-sexual skills and gender role behaviour. The assessment procedures used might be at any of the response levels of physiological reactions to stimuli, observable behaviours, or self-reports (of behaviour, attitudes, feelings, and so on). Generally, but not always, sexual arousal is tapped at the physiological level of assessment, and socio-sexual skills and gender role behaviour at the other two levels.

Direct measures of observable behaviour are less frequently reported than other assessment measures, a point noted by Crawford (1979) in his argument for broad-based behavioural approaches to the assessment and treatment of sexual offenders.

Verbal Assessment

An example of assessment carried out at the verbal level is Cohen *et al.*'s (1971) study of rapists referred for assessment to a Massachusetts treatment centre for dangerous sexual offenders. Four groups of rapist were distinguished. The first group comprised men for whom the act of rape was primarily aggressive. The sexual part of the act was used to harm or degrade the victim. In these cases the offence was often preceded by disagreeable exchanges with a female relative or friend. Sexual excitement was often absent and those parts of the female anatomy normally associated with sexual excitement often became the focus of the offender's aggression. In a second group the offence motive was primarily sexual, aggression only being used to the degree necessary to achieve sexual contact. Offenders in this category remained in a high state of sexual arousal throughout the offence, often achieving orgasm in pursuit of, or upon initial contact with the victim. They were often preoccupied with feelings of sexual inadequacy. The third group comprised offenders for whom sexual and aggressive impulses were interlinked. Sexual arousal was accompanied by feelings of aggression towards the victim, feelings which were projected on to the victim in the form, 'women like to get roughed up'. The extreme example of this group was sexual sadism where the victim may be murdered. In the final group, the act of rape was often carried out in the context of some other antisocial act such as robbery or theft. In these cases the victim was simply present and the act of rape was impulsive and opportunistic.

Psychometric Assessment

A variety of self-report and paper-and-pencil assessment measures of sexual attitudes, sexual preferences and gender identity have been devised for, or used with sexually deviant individuals, including offenders. The need for standardisation on relevant populations and for constant updating of test norms are two major problems. Evidence reviewed by Bancroft (1974) indicates that where this is not done, which is in most cases, questionnaires provide no better results than the much more straightforward procedure of simply asking the individual concerned about his attitudes and preferences. This is not to say that relying on self-reports is necessarily valid, simply that it is no less valid than unstandardised questionnaire data.

Two approaches which have shown promise in terms of their reliability and validity are worthy of particular comment. Feldman *et al.* (1966) devised 'the sexual orientation method' as a means of assessing heterosexual and homosexual interest. Its use in monitoring treatment effects is reported in the account of their therapeutic programme for homosexuals

(Feldman and MacCulloch, 1971). The text is based upon the semantic differential (Osgood *et al.*, 1957) and requires subjects to make paired comparisons of a number of adjectives applied to men and women. The resulting scales of homo, and heterosexual interest have been demonstrated to be both reliable (0·8 test–re-test reliability) and valid (distinguishing well between improved and non-improved patients after treatment).

The second method of interest is the repertory grid (Bannister and Mair, 1968). Subjects are required to indicate differences and similarities between various people known to them. These might include themselves, relatives and, in the case of offenders, their victims. From a series of such comparisons, the major dimensions or constructs along which the subject views the world can be derived. Howells (1979a) used this technique to elicit the constructs of ten heterosexual pedophiles in an American state hospital. In addition to presenting individual profiles, Howells made comparisons between the pedophile group as a whole and a control group of non-sexual offenders. Three main conclusions resulted. First, pedophiles were more likely to view both men and women in terms of a construct of dominance–submission. It seemed that children may be attractive to pedophiles on the social level because of their passivity. Secondly, although pedophiles often saw women in terms of physical appearance rather than other qualities, they were no different in this respect from the control subjects, and Howells argues that this tendency may be a fairly typical reflection of men's perceptions of women. Finally, pedophiles emerged as more preoccupied than the controls with small body build.

Behavioural Assessment

One of the most interesting features of the second, behavioural level of analysis is the relative absence of research when compared with self-report and physiological studies. This is perhaps not surprising given the greater practical requirements of making direct and meaningful behavioural observations. Whereas interviews and physiological testing can usually be carried out in the traditional settings of office or small laboratory, direct observations of social behaviour are more complex to arrange and require either involvement in natural environments or the construction of analogues within the institutional setting.

A number of clinicians working in the area of social skills training with sexual offenders have noted deficiences with, and a lack of relevance to offenders' normal circumstances of many assessment measures currently in use. A number of attempts have been made to derive empirically and validate measures of heterosexual social skills for sexual offenders. Barlow *et al.* (1977) developed a seventeen-item check-list having high inter-rater reliability. Using a procedure of having socially adequate males and socially inadequate sexual deviants talk for about five minutes with a female stooge, it was possible to discriminate accurately between the adequate and inadequate groups. The check-list collapsed into four categories: voice qualities (loudness, pitch, and so on), form of conversation (initiating, picking up cues, and so on), affect (appropriate facial expression, eye contact, and so on) and masculine versus feminine motor behaviour while seated. Separate analyses of the scales' four sub-categories demonstrated that form of conversation and affect were particularly powerful discriminators of the adequate and inadequate groups.

Physiological Assessment

One of the most notable developments in the assessment of sexual offenders has been the use of penile response measures in determining patterns of sexual arousal. Zuckerman's (1971) review concluded that the penile response is the best physiological index of sexual interest in the male. Volume and circumference measures are the most frequently used. Penile measures have been used to assess sexual arousal patterns to both sexual objects (men, girls and so on) and sexual act (rape, masochism, and so on).

The extensive work of Freund and his colleagues (Freund, 1963, 1965, 1967, 1971; Freund *et al.*, 1970, 1974, 1979) has demonstrated that small penile volume changes to rapidly presented visual stimuli (nude figures) provide the basis for a reasonably accurate differential diagnosis of adult heterosexuality versus homosexuality (Freund, 1963) and of heterosexual and homosexual pedophilia (Freund, 1965, 1967). Diagnostic accuracy was found to suffer, however, when subjects were instructed to fake their responses. Whilst 99 per cent of Freund's (1963) homosexual and heterosexual subjects were correctly classified by penile responses when no instructions to fake were given, only twelve of the twenty-four homosexuals and thirty-one of the forty-two heterosexuals were correctly classified when they were given instructions to fake arousal to their non-preferred interest.

Laws and Rubin (1969), using penile circumference measures with four heterosexual subjects, were able to obtain reductions in penile response to a ten-minute erotic film by instructions to inhibit arousal by 'mental means'. Percentage erections fell from between 76 and 80 per cent to between 15 and 22 per cent. Henson and Rubin (1971) obained similar results with five homosexual subjects. They also noted the erection-inhibiting effect of having subjects verbalise about the film clips being shown to them. In an ingenious study using a dichotic listening paradigm, Geer (1974) required subjects to process information being presented to one ear whilst erotic material was being presented to the other ear. Penile erection was monitored and found to decrease as the complexity of information being presented to the first ear was increased. Thus, it appeared that the level of attention being paid to erotic material may be central to the level of arousal generated.

Freund *et al.* (1979) studied the penile volume changes to movie films of 152 'admitting' and 'non-admitting' pedophiles. As expected, diagnostic accuracy with 'admitters' was high (less than 5 per cent errors). For the 'non-admitters', however, about one-third were misdiagnosed, presumably due to the effects of faking. By modifying the form of analysis used, the diagnostic accuracy for non-admitters was enhanced, but only for the homosexual group. It seems that, at least for the present, penile response measures applied as a means of determining sexual orientation with unco-operative subjects are liable to produce errors in a significant minority of cases, Parenthetically, our own research has produced some suggestive evidence that offenders who appear, from questionnaire and self-report data, to be distorting the nature of their sexual interests, often display penile circumference increases *after* relevant stimuli have been removed. The procedure in which this phenomenon occurs involves the alternation of slides depicting deviant and non-deviant material interspersed with periods during which the offender closes his eyes. It is in the 'eyes closed' periods following the presentation of deviant stimuli that these elevated penile responses occur. Although too much cannot be made of this result without further investigation, it is possible that a combination of anxiety relief and deviant imagery during the 'eyes closed' period may be primarily responsible.

In contrast to the approach of Freund *et al.*, in which large numbers of subjects are used to validate penile response measures as a means of diagnostic sexual orientation, Abel and his colleagues have concentrated on a single subject experimental design methodology (Abel and Blanchard, 1976). Using penile circumference measures and audiotaped descriptions of deviant acts, Abet *et al.* (1975) have demonstrated that rapists who report high frequencies of rape fantasies and behaviours responded to audio-taped rape scenes but not scenes depicting consenting sexual intercourse. A second group of rapists who reported interest in both forced and consenting sexual relations responded to both types of scene. Non-rapists only responded to material depicting consenting sexual relations.

Barbaree *et al.* (1979), using similar audiotaped stimulus presentations, compared the penile responses of ten incarcerated rapists and ten students on material depicting consenting sexual intercourse, rape and a violent non-sexual assault. For the non-rapists, descriptions of consenting sexual intercourse produced higher responses than either rape or assault descriptions. For the rapists, however, no differences were evident in their penile responses to rape or consenting sexual intercourse, both of these being higher than their responses to violence. Barbaree *et al.* postulate that a major difference between the rapists and the non-rapists is the rapists' insensitivity to, rather than enjoyment of the elements of violence. Whilst both groups were sexually aroused by the sexual content of rape and consenting sexual intercourse material, only for the non-rapists was sexual arousal inhibited by the violent aspects of the rape material. If confirmed, these results have important implications for treatment.

Abel and Blanchard (1976) argue that there are two advantages of using audiotaped stimuli rather than visual stimuli. First, since some acts and fantasies are both very specific and very violent, verbal descriptions are the only feasible and ethical means of generating appropriate stimulus material. Secondly, the material produced is easily manipulated so that stimulus refinements can be made and increasingly subtle aspects of the offender's interests teased out. Although a subject may report that one part of a sequence is the most arousing for him, the clinician can determine which parts of the sequence actually generate the greatest responses. Second and third generation audiotapes can be constructed from elaborations of the most potent sections of each previously presented sequence.

Bancroft (1971), reviewing applications of penile response measures, concludes that their use as a means of diagnosing sexual orientation is suspect for two reasons. First, cognitive mediational processes can, as reported earlier, play an important part in determining penile responses. Processes such as distraction and non-erotic thoughts can be used by uncooperative subjects to inhibit their sexual arousal. Secondly, it seems likely that the reverse effect, that is, the stimulation of penile responses, could be achieved by subjects engaging in erotic fantasies not associated with the stimuli being presented. Understanding how cognitive and physiological processes interact in offender or patient groups, and under different testing conditions, is still far from clear. Of importance to investigate further would seem to be the effects upon an offender's sexual profile – as determined by his penile responses to sexual stimuli – of factors such as his perceptions of the degree of pressure on him to co-operate, his attitudes, and his perception of other people's attitudes about his offence behaviour. Also important might be the nature of such aspects of his cognitive style as his ability to engage in imagery.

To summarise, there is evidence that even small penile responses to erotic stimuli, particularly movie films or videotapes (Abel and Blanchard, 1976), are useful in four ways. First, they can confirm sexual orientation and compare general categories of sexual interest among various groups of patients and offenders. Caution is, however, required in using penile measures for diagnostic purposes with subjects whose level of co-operation is suspect. Secondly, the specific sexual cues to which individual offenders respond can be isolated by a process of progressive stimulus refinement. This is therapeutically valuable as even co-operative offenders may not always be able to pinpoint verbally the most potent features of their arousal to offence-related material. Thirdly, changes in penile response can be used to monitor treatment progress and contribute to the clinical evaluation of its success. Finally, there is some evidence that changes in penile response during treatment may be a good indication that treatment effects will generalise and be maintained.

Treatment

Levels of Intervention

As in the assessment area, interventions directed at reducing sexual offending can be viewed on a number of levels. At the widest, sociological level, the design of our environment, the nature of the justice system and the relative provisions of various educative, treatment and counselling services are all areas of potential intervention. Changes in any of these can, in a sense, be seen as a treatment response by society to the problem of sexual crime. At the opposite end of the spectrum is the most specific level of intervention, that of modifying the behaviour of individual offenders. As we have seen, this is the least significant level of intervention in terms of sexual crime as a whole. It is, however, of major importance when we consider the small group of dangerous and repetitive sexual offenders.

Within the behavioural framework, the treatment of individual offenders will follow, in the first instance, from two considerations. First, the definitions of problems and goals, a process in which both the offender and the therapist are involved, will specify as clearly as possible the behaviours to be eliminated and those to be developed. Secondly, the functional relationships between the offender's desired and undesired behaviours and factors within his environment will be sought. The process of behavioural, or functional analysis which works to this end will seek to identify those assets and deficits within the individual's behavioural repertoire and factors within his environment which maintain deviant behaviours and those which will assist the development of alternative, target, behaviours. It is on the manipulation of these personal and environmental factors that treatment will concentrate.

Howells (1981a) has shown that public attitudes towards sexual offending are an important context to both the offender's desire for treatment and the treatment process itself. If sexual offending were neither legally nor socially proscribed, it is unlikely that many offenders currently receiving treatment would wish to change their behaviour. It is particularly important, therefore, that legal and ethical issues surrounding treatment should be very clearly laid out. Various writers, Crawford (1981) and Marshall *et al.* (1977) being two recent examples, have stressed the need for informed and non-coercive consent, particularly given the irreversibility of some therapeutic procedures, before the treatment of sexual offenders can be regarded as ethically sound. Others, of course, might equally argue that the rights of the offender are secondary to those of the victim to demand retribution and the need to protect potential future victims from harm.

Castration and Chemical Treatments

The ethical issues surrounding the treatment of sexual offenders are perhaps most sharply brought into focus with the medical procedures of castration and anti-libinal medication. Stürup (1968, 1972) in Denmark has advocated castration as the 'total treatment' for sexual recidivists. Stürup (1972) reports that of 900 castrated sexual offenders, only 1 per cent were reconvicted for sexual offences during the following thirty years. This compared with a 24 per cent sexual reconviction rate for non-castrated offenders. A number of points need to be made (Marshall *et al.*, 1977). First, since Stürup calculated that 75 per cent of his total group were unlikely to re-offend without treatment, many of his treated cases must have been needlessly castrated. Secondly, whilst Stürup refers to this treatment as being appropriate for sexual recidivists, 18 per cent of his patients had never been convicted of a sexual offence and 40 per cent had only one such conviction. Hence, 58 per cent did not meet his own criteria for treatment suitability. Thirdly, although Stürup emphasised that his patients voluntarily underwent castration, the fact that they were in effect offered, and subsequently achieved early release – about two-thirds within one year of the operation – raises serious doubts about the interpretation of their voluntary status. Fourthly, even if the stated goal of eliminating the offender's sex drive is accepted ethically, there is no reason to suppose that this is necessarily a key area for treatment. Fifthly and finally (Crawford, 1981), there are a number of side-effects of castration, including hip and breast enlargement, diminution of facial and bodily hair, and hot flushes and sweating. Unlike Stürup, who claims that his patients are generally satisfied with castration, Langelüddeke (1963) in Germany reported that only about 50 per cent of his 1,600 group of castrated offenders were satisifed with their post-operative condition.

Like castration in their aim of eliminating or reducing sexual drive are the various forms of chemical treatment. There are four types of drug which have been used to suppress sexual behaviour. These are oestrogens, progestogens, anti-androgens and tranquillisers. Bancroft (1977) concludes that the anti-androgen Cyproterone acetate is probably the drug of choice at the present time. The tranquilliser Benperidol, Bancroft notes, sometimes has advantages because of its mild sedative effect but this can also be a disadvantage.

In summary, physical treatments of sexual offenders range from the 'overkill' of castration to the weaker and less harmful Cyproterone acetate, the anti-libinal drug in most common use at the present time. It will be the exception rather than the rule that physical treatments alone will meet the needs of the offender. Perhaps two of the most valuable functions of drugs such as Cyproterone acetate are, first, as part of broader-based therapy programme in which its effects provide a period of sexual quiescence during which other forms of treatment have time to begin taking effect and, secondly, in helping elderly offenders for whom the desire for, or feasibility of establishing alternative sexual behaviours to offending is low because of their age.

Psychological Treatments

A distinction is often made between psychodynamic therapies, including psychoanalysis, and behavioural treatments. At one level this is a reasonable distinction to make; the theoretical underpinnings and development of behaviour therapy does indeed set it apart from the psychodynamic therapies. Pacht (1976) notes that most of the psychodynamic therapies used with sexual offenders were initially developed for use with other groups. Typically, evidence presented to support the efficacy of such techniques is experiential rather than research based, or else lacking altogether. This is not necessarily to say that all such approaches are ineffective, simply that the necessary evidence does not exist.

Empathic Therapeutic Relationships

Abel et al. (1976) cite evidence that the establishment of an empathic relationship between offender and therapist can be an important aspect of therapeutic effectiveness. This is true of both psychotherapy and behaviour therapy. The precise nature of the mechanism involved is unclear. Some therapists emphasise the importance of the offender feeling accepted and achieving a sense of his own worth, whilst others stress the importance of the offender being able to express suppressed emotions in the accepting climate of the therapeutic situation. Marshall *et al.* (1977) note the prevalence of poor self-esteem amongst sexual aggressives and regard this as both a contributory factor to their offending and an important focus of therapy. Again, the existence of an empathic relationship between offender and therapist would seem likely to be an important, if not an essential ingredient of successful treatment.

Socio-Sexual Skills

Heterosexual skills, or more precisely those skills, whether heterosexual or homosexual, relevant to achievement of the offender's non-deviant sexual goals, is another important focus for therapy. Group psychotherapeutic approaches have recognised, and introduced into their programmes the opportunities for interaction between offender and female members of staff. Some group therapy programmes have in fact made such interactions a requirement. Working with rapists in a US state hospital, Boozer (1975), for example, viewed the achievement of socially skilled relation-ships with females as an essential ingredient of treatment and employed female-only attendants in her treatment programme for rapists. Behaviour therapy has arrived at similar conclusions relatively later in its history and by a more circuitous route.

Crawford and Allen (1979) in a British Special Hospital and Perkins (1977) in a prison and outpatient setting carried out social skills training with sexual offenders. Trainees were given instructions on how to improve their performance, watched models of appropriate behaviour, carried out role plays with male and female therapists and received feedback on their performance. Using a variety of behavioural observations, ratings and questionnaire data, Crawford and Allen demonstrated significant changes in social behaviour which were maintained on a two-year follow-up. How-ever, since the offenders in question remained incarcerated throughout treatment and follow-up, neither the degree of generalisation of skills beyond the hospital setting nor the effect of improved social skills on subsequent sexual offending could be assessed. Perkins compared data from the treatment group with that from a quasi-control group of non-offenders. The offenders after treatment resembled the quasi-controls on the self-report measures and some of the measures of verbal and non-verbal behaviour from the videotaped interactions with the stooges. Perkins's group of offenders continued to be seen in the community and are now part of a long-term programme of treatment evaluation.

In a similar vein, Gordon *et al.* (1977) noted that, whilst it is known that many rapists find difficulty establishing and maintaining appropriate socio-sexual relationships, there are no readily available definitions of what would constitute appropriate socio-sexual behaviour for each offender. Therapists often resort to educated guesswork in deciding which behaviours to assess and train. Group-based social skills programmes can, to the extent that not all group members are similarly deficient and un-knowledgeable, deal with this by tapping their differing experiences from within similar social backgrounds. In contrast to the experimentally constructed social interaction norms of Barlow *et al.* (1977), Gordon *et al.* (1977) adopted an ethological approach to study the social interactions of naïve pairs of subjects and thereby generated normative patterns of behaviour. The empirically determined categories of verbal and non-verbal behaviour which resulted were then used to assess the social performance of sexually aggressive offenders. By not predefining the female half of the interaction this approach moves much nearer to the natural circumstances which will face the offender when he leaves the therapeutic situation.

In summary, the area of socio-sexual skills requires much more extensive investigation before a high level of relevance to sexual offenders can be claimed. Social skills training with sexual offenders often not only makes assumptions about what are, and are not appropriate skills in the natural environments of the offenders receiving training but also uses female stooges whose social backgrounds and expectations are very different from those of the women with whom the offenders are likely to interact when training is completed. If the social skills approach is to achieve success it will need to answer a number of questions. First, what are the situations in which the offender is to attempt successful socio-sexual relationships? Secondly, what are the skills appropriate for these situations? Thirdly, how can the training of these skills best be structured within the situations available to the therapist and offender during training? Fourthly, how can generalisation from the therapeutic to the natural environment be best achieved? Often the question of generalisation appears to be an afterthought in social skills training programmes, receiving attention only after the training is completed. Adopting a rigorous behavioural approach, the therapist should in fact make the structuring of generalisation into the treatment programme one of his first considerations.

Sexual Arousal: Suppression

An important therapeutic goal with sexual offenders is the reduction of deviant, and the increase of non-deviant sexual arousal. A distinction between those procedures which suppress, and those which increase sexual arousal is, upon examination of the evidence, not a totally clear one. A notable example is *aversion therapy* in which unpleasant stimulation of some form is associated with some aspect of the offender's deviant arousal. Crucial variations in aversion therapy are the nature of the stimuli used (slides, films, audiotapes, imagination, and so on), the noxious stimulation with which sexual stimuli are associated (chemically induced nausea, electric shocks, unpleasant smells, and so on) and the learning paradigm adopted (punishment, classical conditioning, anticipatory avoidance conditioning, and so on). In some studies using electrical aversion therapy with sexual deviants and offenders (Bancroft, 1970; Callahan and Leitenberg, 1973), it has been reported that increases to non-deviant, usually adult heterosexual, stimuli have occurred during aversion therapy designed to suppress responses to deviant stimuli. In other studies this phenomenon has been absent (Tanner, 1974) or even reversed (McConaghy, 1969), in that some patients actually had their deviant arousal increase more than their non-deviant arousal following aversion therapy.

Marshall *et al.* (1977) stressed the need to relate the choice of sexual and noxious stimuli to be used in aversion therapy to the nature of the offender's problem. He notes that, with slides and movie films for example, the offender's freedom to elaborate his sexual fantasies can be constrained or even suppressed altogether by the stimulus materials. Hallam and Rachman (1976), reviewing the evidence on aversion therapy, conclude that explanations of its effect purely in terms of conditioning principles is unsatisfactory. It is rare that patients treated by aversion therapy develop the kinds of conditioned anxiety which would be predicted from the conditioning literature. More usually is a reported disinterest in, or an altered perceptual quality of the deviant object or act to which the patient has been averted. Hallam and Rachman conclude that aversion therapy is a complex phenomenon in which the total therapy situation is probably relevant. Its effects are still far from clearly understood.

Covert sensitisation (Cautela, 1967) is a type of aversion therapy in which the stimuli to be averted and the aversive stimulation are both imaginal. Typically, the patient imagines the deviant act, then follows this with some imagined unpleasantness such as an arrest or an illness. While some studies have shown this procedure to be effective (Callahan and Leitenberg, 1973; Barlow *et al.*, 1969), Christie *et al.* (1978) have reported a failure of the procedure to modify the deviant fantasies of sexually aggressive offenders. This failure, they postulate, may be a function of sexually aggressive offenders' poor imaginal abilities and their immunity to many of the unpleasant consequences they were required to associate with the deviant imagery. It may also be that the procedure works best with sexual deviants whose levels of sexual arousal do not exceed some critical level, about which imagined aversive consequences cease to be effective in suppressing that sexual arousal.

A further variation on the aversion theme is *shame aversion therapy* reported by Serber (1970). In this procedure the patient is required to act out his deviant behaviour in front of therapist aids who act disapprovingly or ridicule him. These unpleasant consequences of the patient's behaviour proved successful, at six month follow-up, in suppressing the deviant activities of seven of the ten sexual offenders treated by Serber and Wolpe (1972). Whilst the procedure can be readily used with deviant activities such as exhibitionism, it is difficult to adapt in any realistic way to the treatment of rapists and pedophiles. Furthermore, since many sexually aggressive offenders are already low in confidence and self-esteem (Marshall *et al.*, 1977), this procedure runs the risk of being counter-productive with such patients.

A fourth approach to decreasing deviant sexual arousal is *satiation therapy* reported by Marshall and Barbaree (1978). The procedure is based on the observation that sexual fantasies, pornography and routine sexual activities lose their erotic appeal with repetition. Marshall and Barbaree hypothesised that if repetitions of specific sexual acts or fantasies lead to boredom and extinction, then it might be possible to extinguish whole classes of behaviour, such as sexual aggression, by having offenders verbalise deviant fantasies whilst masturbating for long periods of time. For the three pedophile cases for whom data has so far been reported, the procedure has proved to be highly effective.

Sexual Arousal: Enhancement

Barlow (1973) reviewed the clinical and experimental evidence on procedures for increasing non-deviant sexual arousal and behaviour. Procedures were grouped under nine headings: aversion, aversion relief, systematic desensitisation, social retraining, pairing, masturbatory conditioning, fading, shaping and exposure. Of those procedures specifically geared to increasing heterosexual arousal, one of the most frequently reported at the time of Barlow's review was *aversion relief*. The procedure is based on pairing the cessation of an aversive stimulus, for example electric shock, with heterosexual stimuli to which the patient's sexual responsiveness is to be increased. Thorpe *et al.* (1963) and Feldman and MacCulloch (1965) note the apparent effect of the procedure in creating feelings of relief which then become associated with the heterosexual stimuli being presented. Barlow (1973) and Abel and Blanchard (1976) point out that the effects of the procedure have rarely been tested separately from the effects of aversion alone; it was noted earlier that, for reasons which are not altogether clear, aversion therapy can sometimes enhance sexual arousal to non-deviant stimuli. When independent assessments of aversion relief have been made, the procedure has failed to prove effective.

Barlow and Agras (1973) reported an ingenious approach to increasing heterosexual arousal in homosexual patients by the technique of *fading*. A heterosexual slide was superimposed on a homosexual slide to which the patient had produced a penile response. By gradually decreasing the light level of the homosexual slide and fading in light from the heterosexual slide, it proved possible to maintain the patient's penile response in the presence of the heterosexual slide. The result of this procedure with three homosexual patients suggested that it had some effect on increasing arousal to heterosexual situations but no effect on reducing homosexual interest. Laws (1974) has reported an automated version of this fading procedure, with which two pedophiles were treated. The fading in of non-deviant stimuli continued as long as the patient's sexual response was maintained at some pre-set level, usually 70 per cent full erection. Fourteen sessions had some effect in increasing non-deviant arousal but this tended to be lost on follow-up. The evidence for the power of this procedure is very limited.

One of the most commonly used procedures for increasing non-deviant sexual arousal is *masturbatory conditioning* or 'orgasmic reconditioning' (Marquis, 1970). McGuire *et al.* (1965) noted the importance of early sexual experiences in determining an individual's subsequent sexual interest and behaviour. Seventy-five per cent of fifty-two sexually deviant individuals reported using similarly deviant masturbation fantasies. Frequently, masturbatory conditioning is used in conjunction with other techniques such as aversion therapy (Marshall, 1973; Marshall and McKnight, 1975; Matthews, 1977; Perkins, 1977) and so specific effects cannot be evaluated. In one controlled study of masturbatory conditioning alone, Abel *et al.* (1973) successfully treated a patient with sadistic fantasies by having him alter these fantasies during masturbation. The patient was required to masturbate whilst verbalising the fantasies being used. These fantasies were tape-recorded and content analysed. Results showed that percentage penile erections to the sadistic audiotapes fell from 80 per cent to between 10 and 20 per cent after treatment and at follow-up. Penile erections to non-deviant material rose from between 10 and 20 per cent to between 60 and 70 per cent, and only fell to 50 per cent at follow-up. One factor which may be relevant to the success or otherwise of this procedure is the degree of therapist control over the patient's behaviour. The comments of some of the offenders in our own programme suggest that poor motivation, either through reluctance to lose currently pleasurable deviant fantasies or through a low level of recognition of the relationship between masturbatory conditioning and the achievement of ultimate treatment goals, may play an important part in determining therapeutic success. A corollary to this seems to be that some offenders who report using the procedure in an active and positive way begin reporting increased motivation to cease offending and establish non-deviant behaviour. It may be that, like aversion therapy, masturbatory conditioning achieves its effects by a complex interaction between conditioning and cognitive processes.

The reluctance of some offenders in treatment to lose their currently reinforcing deviant fantasies is a major reason for Marshall *et al.* (1977) and Laws (1980) amongst others advocating that the first line of approach in modifying the sexual arousal patterns of sexual offenders should be to increase non-deviant arousal and only after this is achieved moving on to eliminate deviant arousal. A technique which has shown some promise in increasing non-deviant arousal without interfering with deviant arousal is *exposure*. The procedure is simply that the patient is exposed to highly erotic non-deviant stimuli such as films and slides. Herman *et al.* (1974) report a successful outcome with four homosexual patients using this technique. Post-treatment heterosexual arousal was maintained after exposure to a ten-minute nude female movie film.

A number of cases have been reported of *biofeedback* being used to increase penile responses to non-deviant stimuli. Both auditory and visual feedback to the subject of his physiological state have been employed. Herman and Prewett (1974) found the method effective in increasing the penile responses of impotent patients. Barlow *et al.* (1975), on the other hand, reported an unsuccessful outcome with three homosexuals. The question of patient motivation may again be relevant. The desire of patients to overcome impotence, as in the first study, may have been stronger and less complex than the motivation of homosexual patients to change their sexual orientation, the goal of the second study.

An approach to enhancing non-deviant sexual arousal patterns which brings us back full circle to the social treatments, is *systematic desensitisation*. This procedure is designed to eliminate avoidance of heterosexuality, in patients for whom this is a problem, through a process of gradual exposure to the anxiety-provoking aspects of the heterosexual situation. On the basis that heterosexual anxiety can contribute to the maintenance of homosexual behaviour, Bancroft (1970) compared aversion therapy (to decrease homosexual arousal) and systematic desensitisation (to reduce heterosexual anxiety) in homosexual patients. As predicted, desensitisation had the desired effect of increasing heterosexual arousal. Similar results from desensitisation have been reported by Bieber *et al.* (1963) with homosexuals. In only one of the thirty-six sexual offenders in the treatment programme reported by Perkins (1977) was heterosexual anxiety such that systematic desensitisation was called for. The patient in question was a heterosexual pedophile who displayed severe anxiety to female breasts and pubic hair.

Cole (1980, personal communication) has reported the use of a form of 'in vivo' desensitisation for sexually and socially inadequate non-deviant males. This *surrogate therapy* involved patients being guided to satisfactory sexual intercourse with female surrogate partners who were suitably trained and motivated to help and encourage the patient. With these experienced and reassuring surrogate partners, Cole's patients only rarely failed to achieve satisfactory sexual intercourse. Interestingly, Cole reports that for patients whose primary social deficiency was one of social confidence, the achievement of a satisfactory heterosexual experience led to marked improvements in social functioning which were maintained if consolidated by satisfactory sexual relationships in the natural environment. If such consolidation did not occur, patients' social confidence and functioning were liable to decline. If confirmed, this finding points to the possibility, if not always the desirability, of 'short-circuiting' the usual therapeutic practice of training social skills before tackling sexual skills. Cole reports an unsuccessful outcome with the one sexually deviant individual, a heterosexual pedophile, treated by this procedure, whilst Kohlenberg (1974) reported a successful outcome with a homosexual pedophile.

An important treatment approach which brings together various aspects of the sexual, social and socio-sexual therapies is *sex education*. A number of treatment programmes for sexual offenders include some form of sex education as part of broader-based treatment packages. Crawford (1981) specifically examined sex education as a therapeutic intervention and established the effectiveness of an eight-week education programme in increasing sexual knowledge, decreasing sexual anxiety and conflicts and improving self-image. Woodward (1980) has demonstrated similar effects in an English borstal setting.

Self-Control Procedures

Lee-Evans (1978) reviewed the possible uses of self-control procedures with sexual offenders. There are three stages involved. The first, self-monitoring, requires the patient to become aware of the circumstances or triggering cues which have elicited past behaviour. The second stage, self-evaluation, is one in which the patient learns to recognise what is appropriate or inappropriate behaviour in a given situation. The final stage, self-reinforcement, involves the patient rewarding himself in some way for taking appropriate courses of action. Evidence on the applicability of this approach with sexual offenders is still limited. Crawford (1981) reports work at the South Florida State Hospital where patients are required to recognise, and then act upon 'early warning signals' in their behaviour which have previously led on to sexual offending. In our own treatment programme, two indecent exposure offenders were treated in the community using this approach. With one offender the technique proved strikingly more successful than with the other. The difference between the two individuals concerned again appeared to rest on motivation to apply the technique. In terms of the number of failed out-patient appointments, the unsuccessful case was, paradoxically, the better attender. It simply seemed to be that his conceptualisation of treatment began and ended with interviews with the therapist; he could not, or would not carry over into the natural environment agreed courses of action. The other patient, in contrast, appeared to welcome the greater responsibility he perceived as stemming from the self-control procedure, remembered the therapeutic instructions and put them into practice with some success. Self-control appears to offer a number of promising possibilities for the treatment of sexual offenders, not least of which is the effect it may have upon offenders' perceptions of themselves and their responsibilities in the treatment situation.

Discussion

Available evidence suggests that most dangerous sexual offending is both rare, in terms of criminal statistics, and unpredictable. There are, however, categories of sexual offender who either habitually carry out serious sexual attacks or else who escalate to serious sexual offending from relatively minor transgressions.

Some serious sexual offenders display in objective testing of sexual arousal, predilections for the same types of sexual object or sexual act represented in their offence behaviour. The histories of, and treatment experiences with such offenders indicate that these deviant sexual interests have been reinforced by both masturbation fantasies and the commission of sexual acts of a similar kind. To the extent that masturbation fantasies and sexual acts are stimulated by the individual's sexual interest, which is in turn orgasmically reinforced by the acts of masturbation and offending, something of a vicious circle exists at this psychophysiological level of the offender's behaviour. A somewhat wider vicious circle, if it can be put like that, exists in the interaction between the offender's deviant sexual interests, as measured by his penile responses, and his socio-sexual behaviour in general. At its simplest, a socially inadequate individual who may, as a result of this inadequacy, have become involved in sexual liaisons with children or sexual attacks on women will, in so doing, run the risk of both generating deviant sexual interest in the offence behaviour and further remove himself from the classes of socio-sexual behaviour which he might ideally wish to pursue.

Much of the work cited has emphasised the importance of 'broad based' approaches to treatment. Crawford (1981), for example, stresses the importance of equipping the sexual offender with the knowledge and skills which he will need in order to engage in socially acceptable sexual behaviour. Morever, Crawford suggests that these aspects of treatment should be sequenced so as to meet the offender's needs in the order in which they will need to be met within the community. When first released from custody, for example, the offender will need the necessary social skills to interact successfully with both men and women. He will then need a sufficient level of sexual interest in women, if adult heterosexuality in his goal, to motivate movement towards the next stage in the socio-sexual encounter. Once friendships with the opposite sex have been established and sexual relationships become a possibility, he will then need the necessary sexual knowledge and skill to interact successfuly on this level.

The assessment and treatment literature which has been reviewed points to a number of therapeutic approaches which may be relevant for dangerous sexual offenders. Some have been used with such offenders whilst others have so far only been explored with relatively minor offenders or non-offending sexual deviants. An important point may be that although sexual offenders are likely to have problems on a number of the different treatment levels reviewed, physiological, perceptual, social, these problems will vary both in degree and in their centrality to the offender's offence behaviour. To the extent that treatment concentrates on the most central and most severe problems, re-offending may be prevented. The offender may, of course, continue to suffer from the less central, untreated problems but these may gradually disappear as a result of the offender's freedom for re-offending and reconviction. The converse situation might arise where the offender's less severe and less central problems are dealt with during treatment but where more fundamental problems remain to erode the effects of treatment and lead to re-offending.

Crucial to this issue is the way in which assessment and treatment is carried out. Simply to identify the offender's problems in the form of a check-list, deviant sexual interest, poor social skills, and so on, and to then set about treating these problems, either by giving equal weight to each in some random order or deciding emphases and orders of priority on the basis of some implicit model of what might be relevant to the offender, is perhaps unlikely to be the most cost-effective way to proceed. The particular and unique way in which each offender's assets and deficits have developed historically and the way in which they functionally interrelate in the context of his present environment are, when available to the therapist, guidelines which can play an important part in determining the order and priority of the various therapeutic interventions available.

At the time of writing, a relatively minor offender who exemplifies many of the problems earlier discussed was referred to the author for an assessment of his 'dangerousness' and suitability for treatment. Friendly, overweight and somewhat below average intelligence, the young man in question explained that he has always been concerned about the small size of his penis. He was ridiculed at school and remembers a doctor commenting on his penis, 'a bit small for his age', when he was being examined as a child in connection with his obesity. His shyness was particularly pronounced with girls and this was not helped by the rigidity of his father's attitudes about relationships and sexuality. Depressed by his social and sexual problems, the patient gravitated towards heavy drinking and, by his account, committed burglaries in a residential area for money and sexual excitement. He entered casual sexual relationships, often when drunk, with female acquaintances but these were usually terminated as a result of derogatory comments made about the size of his penis. He has been an in-patient of a number of psychiatric hospitals because of his heavy drinking and suicide attempts.

At the time this man was seen, he retained hopes that he might eventually establish a satisfactory sexual relationship, having had one such relationship in the past, but also described considerable hostility towards women. His masturbation fantasies centred on rape and, recently, on killing his victim at the point of orgasm. He expressed motivation to succeed with relationships and motivation to pursue possible therapeutic strategies such as altering his masturbation fantasies and avoiding the kinds of casual sexual relationships which are likely to reinforce his negative self-image. However, a number of the factors crucial to his improvement or deterioration lie outside the control of any therapeutic intervention, notably the reactions of females he will encounter. Assessment of his 'dangerousness' cannot therefore be made with any degree of certainty since his future behaviour rests to an unpredictable degree on the unpredictable behaviour of others somewhere in the future. Treatment proceeds in the community for as long as the patient wishes this to happen.

Ethically and technically a number of questions might be asked. If there is any risk of a dangerous sexual offence being committed, should this patient alone decide whether treatment continues? On the other hand, since the patient has, as far as we know, committed no serious offences in the past, should his liberty be restricted on the basis that he exhibits a pattern of behaviour which resembles that found amongst some sexual aggressives? Is treatment a meaningful option to pursue when some factors controlling the patient's subsequent behaviour lie beyond therapeutic control, or does the possibility that a serious sexual offence might be avoided some time in the future make treatment with all its limitations a worthwhile enterprise?

7 Behaviour Rating of 'Dangerous Offenders'

JOHN W. HINTON

This chapter is concerned with the questions of reliability, validity and the generalisation of assessments of behaviour made in institutions, with particular reference to maximum security hospitals and the prediction of dangerousness. The evidence to be considered includes that obtained by my research team at a large English maximum security hospital. One aim of my research project was to assess psychophysiological differences between different categories of offender. At the commencement of the research in 1973, one concern was to differentiate personality types such as 'psychopathic' and 'schizophrenic', and I had originally thought that psychometric assessment could be usefully employed for this purpose.

The limitations of psychometrics as applied to maximum security hospital patients were soon made apparent to me: faking 'socially good' and 'defensiveness' in answering questionnaires (for example, the MMPI) increase with length of detention and the consequent increase of apprehension about release (Black, 1963). This 'fake-good' problem was also illustrated in an investigation (Hinton, 1977) from which it was concluded that personality inventory scales containing questions relating to hostility and paranoia were not just unreliable, they were positively misleading. I concluded from this study that those patients who were really the *most* paranoid and hostile (judging by their psychophysiological reactions) were those who reported the *least* paranoia and hostility. Thus, I decided to develop a nurses' behaviour rating scale. The outcome was the OBRS (Hinton, 1975), which is summarised in Table 7.1.

Table 7.1 *Special Hospitals Objective Behaviour Rating Scale (OBRS) Developed on and Applied to Broadmoor Security Hospital Patients*

Scale 1:	Belligerent, anti-authority, antisocial behaviour.
Scale 2:	'Psychotic disorientation': communication and perceptual abnormalities.
Scale 3:	Social withdrawal.
Scale 4:	Personal hygiene.

Although finally intended for use as a research instrument on admission patients, the behaviour rating scales had to be developed on a sample of institutionalised patients whose lengths of incarceration ranged from two to twelve years (Hinton, 1975). Some pilot research on the validation of these behaviour rating scales has been reported, against using a sample of institutionalised patients. There was some weak correlational and other statistical evidence suggesting a relationship between 'antisocial behaviour' and 'withdrawal' dimensions and case record criteria of 'murderousness' (Hinton *et al.*, 1978). This relationship (see Figure 7.1) was interpreted in terms of the ideas of Blackburn and Megargee: an 'impulsivity–overcontrol' dimension was postulated running diagonally from 'anti-social outgoing' to 'socialised withdrawn'. This evidence was however based on small samples and it was intended to conduct further studies, to validate and test for generalisation of these results to a larger sample of admission patients. The outcomes of these studies are considered later in this chapter.

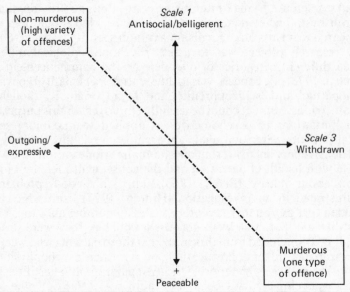

Source: Hinton, Webster and O'Neill, 1978.

Figure 7.1 *A suggested relationship between case record criteria of dangerousness and behaviour rating dimensions of antisocial behaviour and social withdrawal.*

Blackburn (1979) reports research on a behaviour rating scale which he and Lee-Evans developed at Rampton Security Hospital for the less intelligent and subnormal. This instrument was called the Nurses' Observation Scale (NOS). The first factor on the NOS was labelled 'Psychopathy' (antisocial behaviour) and this linked nonconformity with aggression. The second factor, labelled 'Social withdrawal', loaded heavily on items concerned with social interaction.

There is a large variety of factors which could lead to aggressive inter- action of a patient with the authorities in a hospital ward, that is, the behaviour raters. One could therefore question whether it is correct for the first factor on the NOS to be labelled 'Psychopathy'. Rather than considering this factor as 'antisocial aggression' perhaps it would be more correct to conceptualise it as an 'anti-authority' or 'anti-hospital regime' dimension. The same would apply to the first scale on the rating instrument which I developed, which is labelled 'belligerent, antisocial and anti-authority behaviour' and which has many similarities to the NOS 'Psychopathy' factor. This notion of a 'disobedience' factor in behaviour ratings will be discussed at greater length later.

The reliability of the NOS Scales 'Psychopathy' and 'Social withdrawal' have been reported as fairly high by Blackburn and Lee-Evans (unpublished). Working on the means of two raters over a twelve-month period, test/retest reliabilities were found to be 0·76 for 'Psychopathy' and 0·80 for 'Social withdrawal'. The corresponding reliabilities were 0·56 and 0·71 where the second ratings were carried out after an interval of approximately two years with different pairs of raters. The marked drop in reliability of the psychopathy scale as compared to social withdrawal could reflect changes in patients' reaction towards different authority figures with different styles of maintaining discipline. An investigation using analysis of variance techniques indicated the relative contribution of 'persons' and 'settings', and the investigators concluded that while the 'settings' effect for the so-called psychopathy scale was significant for both medicated and unmedicated subjects, rank ordering remained similar to a considerable extent. However, consistency was found to be higher for the medicated than for unmedicated subjects. It was concluded that the evidence supports personality trait theory. However, this is based on the perhaps doubtful assumption that the environments were significantly different for the various times of rating. The question also arises of whether the greater consistency in the medicated patients could illustrate the effectiveness of pharmacological agents in making behaviour predictable, regardless of the environment.

For the purpose of generalisation and prediction, it is of course important to provide evidence for stable characteristics or personality traits; Blackburn (1979) attempts to do this by examining correlations between self-report psychometric measures (psychopathy and social anxiety) and behaviour rating factors based on nurses' observations (psychopathy and withdrawal). Table 7.2 is a crude summary of the major factors discovered by Blackburn on his SHAPS Inventory.

Table 7.2 *SHAPS Inventory (Blackburn, 1979) Developed from MMPI on Special Hospital Patients: Factors and Main Loadings*

Factor 1 (Psychopathy)
Broadmoor: Lie (−0·79); Impulsivity (+0·94); Aggression (+0·85).
Rampton: Lie (−0·80); Impulsivity (+0·89); Aggression (+0·75).

Factor 2 (Withdrawal)
Broadmoor: Introversion (+0·90); Depression (+0·75); Anxiety (+0·79).
Rampton: Introversion (+0·90); Depression (+0·76); Anxiety (+0·73).

Significant correlations in the region of 0·4 were obtained between a questionnaire factor identified as 'psychopathy' and the NOS factor labelled 'psychopathy'. However, the questionnaire 'social anxiety' score did not correlate to any extent with the 'social withdrawal' rating scale. The evidence for the 'psychopathy' factor cannot be ignored, as it applied to both medicated and unmedicated subjects, though this result only holds on second testing for the medicated subjects. The question arises of whether a 'trait' or a 'state' of antisocial behaviour is being measured. To what extent are measures of hostility, impulsivity, antisocial behaviour and unco-operativeness the interaction between the person, drugs and the environment?

The degree of outward and antagonistic reaction of an individual to the authorities in the maximum security hospital may be the key factor common to both the self-report questionnaire and the rating of psychopathy. This impression is reinforced by the fact that negative lie scale scoring, that is, low faking-good, has the second largest loading on the 'psychopathy' questionnaire factor. It may seem rather incongruous to call this factor 'psychopathy' when a major feature of it appears to be 'honesty' – the *antithesis* of psychopathy. Perhaps a better label would be 'bloody-mindedness'. It seems reasonable to expect that there are people in security hospital who are impulsive, hostile and unco-operative *and* are prepared to react openly against the authorities – to fight against aspects of institutionalisation such as the regimentation.

There are of course considerable implications in labelling people as psychopaths. There is a danger that a behaviour scale developed in an institution may be thought a valid measure of 'psychopathy' and this may be used for predictive purposes, that is, of behaviour after release. There is no reason to expect that an institutional rating scale score of psychopathy would relate to attitudes and behaviour under conditions of freedom. 'Bloody-mindedness' as described above may be one way of maintaining some degree of self-respect in a total institution. A good example of this type of personality could be the prisoner Jimmy Boyle of Barlinnie Prison Special Unit. Because of his violent reaction to prison treatment, he was to a large extent responsible for the development of this small unit, which provides prisoners with a degree of freedom and training in co-operative social behaviour. Until his admission to the Special Unit, Jimmy Boyle had fought violently against prison staff and the degradation of the system. so that he was eventually locked up in the 'cage' at Inverness Prison. There he would undoubtedly have been rated as 'psychopathic' by his custodians. However, in the Special Unit his reaction to a completely changed regime became very different, and I have no doubt that staff there would have rated him as non-psychopathic in behaviour. With reference to the case just described, I would like to suggest that characteristics such as dominance and self-assertion may well be fairly stable and consistent – but given a certain type of restricted detention, aggressive and impulsive behaviour may emerge as a protection of the personality.

I would now like to consider further the question of the stability of rated behaviour, with reference to some of the results I have obtained from behaviour ratings made on newly admitted patients at a maximum security hospital. The initial ratings made by nurses will be compared to ratings made approximately one year later, and to case record criteria of 'incidents' within the institution, psychometric data and psychophysiological indices. (This section is based partly on a paper presented by the author in a symposium at the British Psychological Society Conference, Aberdeen (March 1980).)

The so-called 'objective' behaviour rating scales (OBRS) for security hospital patients (Hinton, 1975) entail the averaging of six nurses' ratings on four scales. The large number of nurses proved to be necessary to overcome the inter-rater variability problem so as to obtain high reliabilities. At this point it is worth mentioning that, in the development of the rating scales, many items had to be cut out due to high inter-rater variability, and the point of interest is that a high proportion of these rejected items were dependent on communication between nurse and patient. This illustrates a major problem in security hospitals, namely, that most nurses see their role as primarily custodial. In fact the need to keep this image is well illustrated by the fact that, in some security hospitals in the UK, the nurses choose to belong to the Prison Officers Union rather than a nurses union, and by their rejection of moves to replace prison officer's uniform with civilian clothes. These attitudes, providing a barrier between patients and staff, place a limit on what can be attained from behaviour rating scales operated by nurses in security hospitals.

The four uncorrelated scales, developed from nurses' ratings on well-institutionalised patients, were given earlier in Table 7.1. These behaviour rating scales were subsequently applied to new patients at the security hospital. It was found that both on the first rating, six weeks after admission, and on a second rating after approximately one year, scale 1 (belligerence) was uncorrelated with the other three scales. These other scales of psychotic disorientation, withdrawal and hygiene, were however intercorrelated on the first and on the second rating to a significant extent, with product moment correlations ranging between 0·51 and 0·58 on both occasions. This could indicate that the only stable differentiation is the crude one between troublesome behaviour and mental illness.

An investigation was next carried out on the stability of the nurses' rating scales scores. High test–retest reliabilities had been obtained on the construction sample of institutionalised patients: taken over a six-week period, these ranged from 0·9 to 0·99 over the four scales. The scale for belligerent behaviour had given the highest reliability. However, on the new sample of admission patients it was found that vast changes in rated belligerent behaviour occurred for many patients over a period of approximately one year. In fact, a correlation of only 0·4 occurred between the initial rating and the subsequent one. Dividing the sample up into those who were rated after nine months, twelve months and fifteen months, it was found that a decrease in correlation with time occurred: from 0·76 down to 0·43 and finally 0·12. Correlations for the other three scales from the first to the second rating were 0·56 for the 'psychotic behaviour' scale 0·34 for 'social withdrawal' and 0·34 for 'personal hygiene'. Thus there seems to be less variability over time in behaviours which could be thought to relate to 'mental illness'. This could be due to the medical labelling effect or a relatively greater stability of psychotic type behaviours regardless of changes in regime or length of incarceration. Overall, however, it looks as though the initial ratings are rather inadequate predictors of behaviour within the institution after a period of a year. This is a somewhat different conclusion to that obtained by Blackburn (1979) on patients of lower intellectual ability at Rampton Security Hospital.

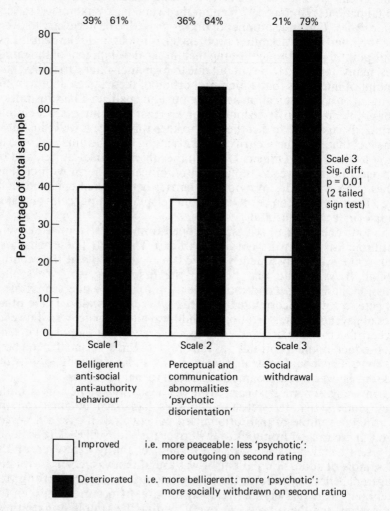

Figure 7.2   *Percentages of security hospital patients 'improved' and 'deteriorated', on three behaviour rating scales, from admission (after six weeks) to approximately one year later (N = 70).*

The question arises of whether the behaviour of the patients is rated as generally 'improving' or 'deteriorating' from just after admission to a year later. Figure 7.2 shows the changes in the mean behaviour ratings from the first to the second one. It gives the percentages of patients reported as show-ing rated 'improvement' and rated 'deterioration' on three of the scales under discussion. Moderate non-significant increases in both belligerence and psychotic symptoms ($p < 0.1$) are illustrated, but there is a statistically significant shift to withdrawal ($p < 0.05$). Does the result indicate that there is a trend towards reactive depression, a resignation to a situation where the individual realises he has little or no control? Perhaps this is the development of 'learned helplessness' (Seligman, 1975). This type of reaction may be more likely in security hospitals where individuals are more vulnerable to pressure (having been classified as mentally abnormal) than in life sentence prisoners. A study by Sapsford (1979) on deterioration and coping in life sentence prisoners suggests that the majority react against 'helplessness training' and find various ways of coping with rather than succumbing to the system. It may well be that over a longer period of time in security hospital some individuals do adapt and find ways of coping ('working the system'?), but others may succumb to the medical label and the close supervision.

Correlations between *changes* in rated behaviour indicate that the increase in 'psychotic' symptoms is correlated very significantly with the increase in withdrawal (0.6). The evidence suggests that a number of those who are rated as withdrawn and somewhat psychotic may become *more* abnormal with the increasing stay in hospital over the first year. It should be noted that patients were not medicated on the Admission Ward and so it was after medication had started that reported 'deterioration' of the psychotic and withdrawal type occurred. Such changes could indicate a 'real' deterioration or might be due to the 'self-fulfilling prophecy' effect of diagnostic labelling, following the final diagnosis at the case conference before leaving the Admission Ward – or could be due to the effects of medication.

In the context of the above-mentioned 'deterioration' effects, it is worth noting that a number of investigations report institutionalisation effects of social withdrawal or depression (Morris and Morris, 1961, 1963; Sluga, 1977), though as Sapsford (1979) points out, other investigators, largely using psychometric methods, find no significant decline in the emotional or intellectual state of long-stay prisoners. However, security hospital, with its medical labelling, high level of staffing and close supervision, is rather different from a prison. It could, therefore be argued that learned helplessness is a more probable response. It is during the first year in the institution that difficulties in institutional adjustment occur, and the inmate may then begin to understand that he is not in a position to demonstrate that he is 'cured'. Many security hospital patients must realise that whatever they do will not affect what happens to them. For some patients the question arises, 'So I am a psychopath – what do I do about it to get cured?' There is no answer to this question, posed in the paper of Treves Brown (1977). Also, the patient with paranoid or psychotic tendencies may have real reason for believing that he is being watched and people are talking about him, so he may thus appear more psychotic and paranoid with increasing incarceration in security hospital.

One check on potential usefulness of behaviour rating scales in security hospitals would be in the prediction of 'incidents' within the institution. One-third of patients in our sample had been 'booked' as being involved in incidents after a period of approximately one year. However, no significant relationships were found between the initial ratings on any of the scales and subsequent reported incidents calculated on an annual basis. This applied both to incidents in which a patient was listed as an instigator and where he had been reported as being at the receiving end. Also, there was no differentiation between patients who were 'receivers' or 'instigators'. Finally, no correlation of significance was found between reported incidents within the institution and behaviour ratings made at a *subsequent* date. These findings are at variance with those given by Davis (1974). Davis's study at Rampton Security Hospital reports a correlation of 0·58 between nurses' ratings and the number of aggressive incidents reported over the following two months. One possible reason for the discrepancy between my results and those of Davis is that the number of incidents reported at Rampton is greater. There may, of course, be more incidents with intellectually subnormal patients. It is possible that behaviour ratings of aggressive behaviour, based on the average of six anonymous nurses' ratings, may be more valid as an indication of 'incidents' than the actual reports in the case records. There are many pressures on custodians in security hospitals which could be expected to lead to incidents not being reported.

A rating scale on aggressive behaviour should not be dismissed because it does not correlate with reported incidents within an institution. However, if it measures a general personality trait which is independent of institutional factors, ratings of aggression and antisocial behaviour should correlate to some degree with past record of convictions (although convictions are far from a complete record of past offending). In a sample of seventy-one new admissions to security hospital, there appeared to be no relationship of behaviour ratings to past record of convictions, variety of convictions, or frequency of convictions. These results are somewhat different to those found on a sample of well-institutionalised patients who were used in constructing and developing the rating scales (Hinton *et al.*, 1978). One possible explanation is that it takes some years for a patient's behaviour to become adjusted to an institution, and only after this adjustment is there a higher correlation with pre-institutional behaviour. This process of adjustment could, however, be affected by nurses knowing the patient's background through their access to the case files. With this point in mind, the results of an unpublished observational study in the female wing of a maximum security hospital may be of interest. This study, which (probably for political reasons) was not cleared for publication or internal circulation by the administration, indicated that knowledge of the patient's diagnosis resulted in nurses 'shaping up' the patient's behaviour to match her classification. Those patients classed as 'mentally ill' or 'schizophrenic' were treated as ill, and antisocial or abnormal behaviour was reinforced by giving the patient treatment – medication, attention and sympathy. By contrast, those patients classified as having psychopathic disorders were given attention of a different kind – punishment and restraint. Life sentence prisoners may have a better chance to adapt and stabilise emotionally as indicated in Sapsford's study (1979).

Returning now to rating scale results, the only significant relationship with case record data was with the self-reported level of past alcoholic intake: heavy drinking was correlated with outgoing behaviour (as opposed to withdrawal) and with lack of psychotic symptoms (both $p < 0.05$).

No significant relationships were found between behaviour rating scale scores and psychophysiological measures usually associated with anxiety and primary psychopathic behaviour (Hinton *et al.*, 1979).

In regard to personality psychometrics, no significant correlations were found between behaviour rating scale scores and scales of psychopathic deviance, hostility and impulsivity (SHAPS Scales) as developed and used by Blackburn. Low but significant correlations were found however between Eysenck's P ('Psychoticism') scale and the rating of psychotic behaviours, while Eysenck's Extraversion Scale correlated significantly in the expected direction with rating of social withdrawal. There is nothing reprehensible in saying (or showing) that one is either extraverted or introverted, so it is not surprising there is some correspondence between rated withdrawal and self-reported social withdrawal.

The psychopathy factor from the NOS (Blackburn, 1979) and the belligerence factor from the OBRS (Hinton, 1975) appear basically similar and the question arises why there is a discrepancy between the two behaviour rating scales in regard to their apparent stability from admission to a year later. There are a number of possible answers. Compared to my sample of high security patients, Blackburn's sample tended to be intellectually subnormal, and less intelligent patients might have been less aware of their predicament, which might lead to greater stability of behaviour. It is also possible that the Rampton regime may have been more stable from admission to the later wards. One marked difference, however, was the drugging policy (Blackburn, personal communication). My study was conducted in a hospital where the policy was to delay the administration of drugs during the period in the Admission Ward, while the policy at Rampton Security Hospital was to apply drugs from the start. This important factor could help to explain the greater stability of behaviour over time reported by Blackburn (1979).

What other factors affect consistency of behaviour in institutions? There are considerable changes in antisocial behaviour in institutions which occur in relation to how the inmate sees his behaviour affecting his release. For instance, it has been noted in a Scottish borstal that the behaviour of many boys deteriorates markedly once they have been given their release date (Stevens, personal communication). It is possible that ratings taken at this time may be more relevant to subsequent behaviour. Sapsford (1979) reports that, for life sentence prisoners, from reception stage to mid-sentence there is a marked reduction in rated anxiety and depression, once they have adapted to their situation and found individual ways of coping. In the security hospital there is the added problem of increasing apprehension due to the gross indeterminacy of the sentence: the longer a patient is detained, the greater his concern about release prospects, so the more he is under pressure to lie (that is, fake good) on questionnaires and the more he is pressured to conform in his behaviour. But does this mean he will conform after release? It seems reasonable to expect that with adult offenders who are experienced and adapted to custodial institutions, prediction of behaviour after release, from behaviour while incarcerated, would be impossible. On the other hand, there is some evidence that with juveniles prediction may be better. Mack (1969) reported a correlation of 0·55 between behaviour ratings of antisocial aggression and subsequent recidivism in young offenders, and more recently (1978) Clarkson reported a twelve-month follow-up study on borstal boys, indicating a significant relationship between actual offending in borstal and subsequent reconviction. Thus prediction in the case of the inexperienced young offender in short-stay institutions may be possible. The 'bloody-mindedness' of youth may however give way to cautious subservience or devious manipulation of the system in older, more experienced inmates, and those serving long sentences.

It seems reasonable to propose that some inmates or security patients who are dominant and outgoing behave 'bloody-mindedly' – being prepared both to 'act-out' against the authorities *and* to endorse antisocial 'psychopathic' attitudes on questionnaires administered by the institution. A particularly interesting group of offenders seems to be those who report very high conformity with high dissimulation scores on questionnaires and who exhibit social withdrawal and extreme obedience within the institution (the 'ideal patient' syndrome?). Individuals with these characteristics would probably be classified as 'overcontrolled' by Megargee and Blackburn. These would seem to be the types who are more likely to have been the domestic killers in real life – the 'bloody-handed' as opposed to the 'bloody-minded'! They are also more likely to be classified as 'mad' or 'psychotic' as opposed to 'bad' or 'psychopathic'. A high proportion of these killers may never be discharged from security hospital, yet of those who are let out a particularly low proportion re-offend. In fact, unlike common criminals in general, those convicted of capital offences show little re-offending. This fact presents problems in the predictive validation of behaviour rating scales developed for assessment of 'dangerousness'.

No prospective validation studies have been carried out using rating scales in security hospitals. Such a study would probably need to be a fifteen-year project covering several establishments. In the unlikely event of such a study being carried out it might be sensible to take ratings regularly over the stay of a patient from admission to release, if it were possible to maintain a constant custodial environment. Correlations with post-release behaviour could then be based not only on the rating scale scores themselves, but on the observed behaviour *trends*. It would, I think, be difficult to make any specific predictions – especially concerning 'dangerousness'.

I conclude on a note of pessimism regarding the usefulness of behaviour ratings in maximum security establishments for the assessment of future re-offending or dangerousness. Apart from almost insuperable problems of administration, there are the problems of institutionalisation and the role of the rater, which is generally accepted as primarily custodial and which does not include communication with patients or inmates except to give orders. It may be agreed that the best predictor of dangerousness would simply be an assessment of the similarity of the environment into which the inmate or patient is being discharged to the environment at the time of his offending. However, such a simple Skinnerian view is I believe inadequate, as it does not take into account relevant organismic factors as discussed in Chapter 11.

Disclaimer

The views expressed in this chapter are those of the author and are not to be taken as those of any government department or institution.

Part Three

New Research Approaches to Characteristics of Dangerous Offenders

8 Biological Perspectives of 'Dangerousness'

DAVID D. WOODMAN

The link between emotions and behaviour, and biological processes occurring at a cellular level is a fascinating one. It is a link which has intrigued physicians for hundreds of years, but attempts to supply scientific explanations have been confined to the present century. However, during the last century Fredericq (1885) noted that compensatory mechanisms were evoked in animals which had been subjected to disturbing events.

The major advance in this field came with the work of Cannon and his associates in the early years of this century. This work began to elucidate the interrelationship between the sympathetic nervous system, the adrenal medulla and emotional stimuli, and provided the basis for our present understanding of the relationship between emotional, physiological and biochemical processes.

At the most basic biochemical level, in order for life to exist the organism must maintain a relatively constant internal environment. Should this vary outside very narrow limits the organism will eventually die. Higher organisms have developed many means of maintaining this internal constancy in the face of widely varying external conditions, and a dynamic biochemical equilibrium is maintained by constant adjustment of the internal needs to the external stimuli.

Any violent change in external conditions which offers a threat to the animal's well-being would overload the normal balancing mechanism. Cannon's work led him to believe that under such conditions the secretions of the adrenal medulla served an emergency function, providing the animal with an enhanced physiological capability to face the threat, or physically escape from it. This process Cannon called the fight or flight syndrome (Cannon, 1929).

Selye (1936) later extended this idea of the metabolic influence over coping behaviour by including the involvement of the adrenal cortex in the long-term response to stress, taking over from the immediate adreno-medullary reaction and facilitating adaptation to the changed situation. The delineation of the fight or flight emotions, however, has not yet been satisfactorily explained. A number of workers in the early 1950s studied the physiological effects produced by emotional stimulation. The general view which emerged from this work was that feelings of anxiety were associated with changes in systolic or diastolic blood pressure, which were attributed to a reduction in peripheral resistance together with an increased cardiac rate and stroke volume as a result of the vasodilation caused by the increased secretion of adrenaline. Aggression on the other hand appeared to be associated with increased peripheral resistance presumed to be the result of vasoconstriction brought about by noradrenaline release. (Ax, 1953; Funkenstein, 1956.)

These findings were strengthened by histochemical evidence indicating that the adrenal medulla contained two types of catecholamine-secreting cells producing predominantly noradrenaline or adrenaline respectively (Hillarp and Hokfelt, 1953); Eranko, 1955).

Further evidence for differential catecholamine release came from studies which indicated that selective catecholamine release could be produced by electrical stimulation of different hypothalamic areas (Redgate and Gellhorn, 1953; Folkow and von Euler, 1954).

Additionally, the study of adrenaline and noradrenaline content of the adrenals of a variety of animal species led Goodall (1951) to the conclusion that aggressive animals had higher noradrenaline concentration than non-aggressive animals. About this time, a number of chemical methods were published which provided a means whereby quantitative measurement of catecholamines could be accomplished (Lund, 1949; Weil-Malherbe and Bone, 1952).

The early work following this transition to quantitative biochemical procedures produced conclusions generally similar to those deduced by the physiologists, that is, correlations between fear and adrenaline secretion and between aggression and noradrenaline release (Elmadjian et al., 1957; Cohen and Silverman, 1958).

More recently, however, opinions have not remained so consistent. While some studies have produced evidence broadly in agreement with the earlier work (Taggart et al., 1969; Carruthers, 1975), others have produced data at variance with these ideas.

Infusions of adrenaline alone or in combination with noradrenaline have been claimed to produce symptoms of apprehension or agitation, while noradrenaline alone produced similar effects of a reduced intensity (Frankenhaeuser, 1971; Levi, 1972).

Other workers using subcutaneous injections of adrenaline have elicited both happy and angry reactions, the manipulation of external factors appearing to be the deciding factor in determining the direction of emotional reaction (Schachter and Singer, 1962).

The interpretation placed on these latter studies has been to cast adrenaline as the principal emotionally active catecholamine exerting its major control over the intensity of the emotional reaction and to ascribe no particular emotional function to noradrenaline. More broadly it has been proposed that any emotional reaction is the result of the combined effects of endocrine, cognitive and environmental factors.

Despite these findings, there remains a considerable amount of evidence pointing strongly to some degree of correlation between both fearful personalities and fear-evoking situations and adrenaline secretion, and between aggressive personalities and anger-evoking situations and noradrenaline (Ekkers, 1975).

An overview of current evidence suggests that a rise in adrenaline secretion and excretion occurs with fearful, novel, unpredictable, or threatening situations, while anger-provoking or familiar but challenging situations elicit similar increases in noradrenaline.

An alternative means of studying the behavioural correlates of catecholamine secretion is to look at the balance between adrenaline and noradrenaline rather than the individual levels of secretion (Gellhorn, 1965). It has been claimed that there is an inverse relationship between the urinary noradrenaline ratio and socio-economic background (Fine and Sweeney, 1968).

This may prove to be primarily an environmental effect rather than a biological one. Working class children are generally believed to encounter harsher living conditions and receive more physical punishment than children from higher social classes (Maccoby et al., 1954; Bayley and Shaefer, 1960).

Correlations between established behaviour and the type of parental discipline encountered during childhood have suggested that the level of physical punishment inflicted by parents is positively correlated with the development of aggressive behavioural tendencies (Becker, 1964; Feshback, 1970).

In the animal field, Levine (1962, 1969) has reported that repeated shocks and handling of young animals interferes with the normal development of anticipatory fear responses. From this he concluded that exposure to regular physical violence when young can have a permanent effect on endocrine and autonomic functions which modify the developing personality.

There is obviously a complex interrelated system which determines what emotional reaction results in any particular individual exposed to a defined stimulus. Equally clear is that monoamines, either in their endocrine or neurotransmitter roles, play a significant part in this system.

Since there is now much evidence to link changes in monoamine dynamics and disposition in a number of forms of mental illness, it is perhaps surprising that relatively little work has been devoted to the biochemical sequelae of stressful stimuli in subjects suffering from various forms of mental illness.

Perhaps more surprising still is the paucity of data specifically relating to socially deviant personalities, diagnosed as mentally ill, where extreme aggression is often a recurring factor.

Most of the previous work done on the biochemical correlates of mental illness has centred on the affective disorders, a population that is relatively large and readily accessible.

Patients suffering from the mental disturbances resulting in criminal deviance account for a much smaller number, and because of the need for secure confinement, are much less accessible, especially to professions other than those immediately concerned with their treatment.

A multidisciplinary study conducted within the Special Hospitals Research Unit (Hinton, 1980) has recently begun to provide data which may give an insight into the biochemical role in the behaviour of violent criminal deviants.

The Research Study

Patients were routinely admitted to a single ward where they remained for six to eight weeks, during which time they did not receive any drugs (as was the hospital practice) unless their behaviour posed a significant threat to either themselves, their fellow patients, or the staff. This initial assessment period allowed time for them to become accustomed to their surroundings and for the effects of any long-term drug to disappear. They were then interviewed and the psychophysiological testing procedures and the aims of the tests were explained. They were asked if they would be willing to take part, on a completely voluntary basis, including the option to withdraw from the experiment at any time. It was also stressed that any information obtained would be used purely for research purposes and would not affect their circumstances within the hospital.

In order to exclude major interfering variables, subjects studied were restricted to males aged between 18 and 45 having no evidence of brain damage or renal dysfunction, no uncorrected sensory defects and having a verbal IQ of greater than 80 (WAIS). Subjects undergoing any form of drug treatment were excluded.

The test session itself used a programme of relatively mild stressors designed to cover as wide a range as might be experienced in everyday life, including difficult perceptual discrimination tests, frustration, mental tests under speed pressure, and so on. The whole programme was taped so that each patient was subjected to an identical series of stimuli and each patient underwent the test on two consecutive days. During the course of the test a number of physiological functions were monitored using surface electrodes connecting the patient to a polygraph recorder in the adjoining room. These measures included heart rate, muscle tension, pulse volume and skin conductance.

Urine samples were collected immediately before and immediately following the test session and blood samples were obtained several days before testing and immediately following the second day's testing. All the testing was carried out between 10 and 11 a.m. to avoid diurnal variation interference. Two control groups were also examined: first a group of healthy volunteers and secondly a group of mental hospital patients who had no record of previous criminal convictions.

There is a large body of evidence now available which indicates that situations which combine uncertainty or unpredictability with the threat of unpleasant stimuli and anticipation of the need for coping behaviour produce similar biochemical responses regardless of the exact form that the anticipated situation takes, for example, subjects anticipating such diverse activities as flying in an aircraft (Euler and Lundberg, 1954), receiving experimentally administered mild electric shocks (Frankenhaeuser and Rissler, 1970) and centrifugation (Goodall and Berman, 1960) all respond by increased adrenaline production and excretion with little alteration in the levels of noradrenaline. Because of this the study reported here was confined to the period of anticipation immediately preceding the induced stress.

Since all the groups studied were anticipating novel, challenging and, to a large extent, uncertain situations, their biochemical responses during anticipation should be quite comparable.

Completely independent reports were produced on the maximum security patients, based on psychophysiological reactivity to stimuli during the test programme. This research assessment, derived from the polygraph recordings, was based on cardiovascular and electromyographic criteria of anxiety and was done without reference to any case record data. Case records were subsequently consulted to determine the details of the crimes for which each patient had been committed. When analyses for the first fifteen maximum security patients had been completed, the biochemical results were compared with the psychophysiological data, and it was found that four patients had urinary noradrenaline to adrenaline ratios markedly higher than the remainder during the period of anticipation preceding the stress-testing programme and that the same patients had notably decreased cardiovascular and electromyographic responses to the stimuli used in the stress programme. At this early stage an abnormally high cut-off point was made arbitrarily at a noradrenaline to adrenaline ratio of 5 : 5. The results for the hyporesponsive group, which we termed BG2, were greater than this value and those for the responsive group, which we termed BG1, were below it. This cut-off point was retained throughout the study during which no hyporesponsive patient fell below the value and only one responsive patient fell above it. All the control subjects had values below 5 : 5 (Woodman and Hinton, 1978b). If we take the security patient sample as a whole and compare it with the control sample as a whole, the proportion of individuals with this high noradrenaline to adrenaline ratio is very significantly greater in the maximum security groups than in the control groups.

Table 8.1   *Urine Catecholamine Values during a Period of Anticipation in the Groups Studied (catecholamine concentration is expressed as n moles/g creatinine)*

Group	N	Adrenaline Mean	S.D.	Noradrenaline Mean	S.D.	NA/A Ratio Mean	S.D.
Normals	18	105·5	21·8	264·6	87·7	2·6	0·7
Mentally ill	19	112·2	16·4	286·8	104·1	2·6	0·9
BG1	44	107·7	45·8	261·4	95·7	2·8	1·5
BG2	14	40·8	10·5	378·2	63·8	10·1	3·3

Table 8.1 shows the mean and standard deviation values for the catecholamines in all of the groups. The adrenaline and noradrenaline distributions are significantly different in the hyporesponsive maximum security group from all the other groups.

Figure 8.1 shows the noradrenaline to adrenaline ratios for the two maximum security hospital groups and the two control groups, that is, the normals groups which is labelled N and the mentally ill group which is labelled M. The distribution of the values from the subjects in the maximum security hospital hyporesponsive group BG2 is almost

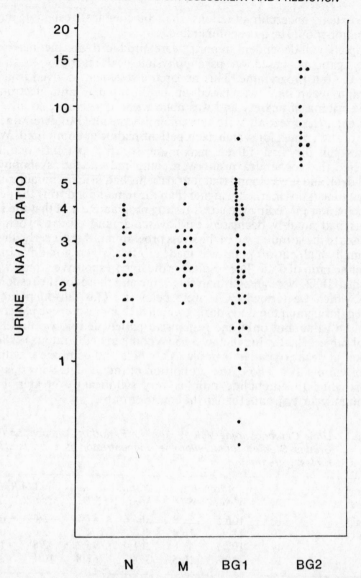

Figure 8.1 *Urine noradrenaline to adrenaline ratio in maximum security hospital patients and control subjects during a period of anticipation.*

completely separate from those of the other groups. The use of the ratio measure would appear to have distinct advantages over the use of concentration measures alone. Although the attempt has been made to reduce the variability of the urinary measures by relating catecholamine excretion to creatinine excretion, the variability of this measure is still quite noticeable, while the values of the ratio measure, which avoids the problem of urine dilution effects, are much more consistent, giving a much more sensitive index of the balance of rates of excretion of the two hormones. Using this index the abnormal catecholamine balance of the group of physiologically hyporesponsive maximum security patients in the anticipatory phase of the experiment is strikingly obvious. This response is totally abnormal. As already indicated, it has previously been shown that situations involving novelty, uncertainty and change normally produce a rise in adrenaline relative to the intensity of the subjective stress reaction caused by the stimulus. This response is modified by situational control, the adrenaline response decreasing with increasing control of the situation. Noradrenaline is not normally affected by these novelty and uncertainty factors. Each of the control groups and the maximum security hospital group who showed no reduction in physiological responses to stress conformed to this pattern, but the physiologically hyporesponsive group showed the opposite response, that is, an increase in noradrenaline in situations of uncertainty characterised in this study by the period of anticipation preceding the stress-testing experiment. Such a response represents an alteration in the character of the biological reaction to stress and not merely a modification of the intensity of the normal reaction.

Under resting or basal activity conditions these subjects produced similar amounts of each catecholamine to the other subjects studied, indicating that the reaction to stress and not the basic catecholamine production is affected.

Similar results were obtained when plasma catecholamines were studied and a high level of correlation between plasma and urinary catecholamines was demonstrated (Woodman, Hinton and O'Neill, 1978a).

The demonstration of this abnormal response was interesting, but to put it into perspective in relation to the subject's long-term behaviour patterns it is necessary to establish whether the response was transient or a constant feature of the individual's biochemical make-up. Thus subjects who remained confined to the hospital and whose treatment did not involve drug therapy were re-examined at varying intervals following the initial test. Sixteen subjects were retested after intervals varying between four and twenty-five months after the admission testing. Five of these subjects had originally shown the abnormal biochemical and physiological responses to testing, and the remainder the expected response. In each case the subject's second test results confirmed the initial data (Woodman, 1979a).

Although the numbers studied were small, the fact that the abnormal reaction could be elicited for a second time in each subject suggests that the reaction may well be a permanent stable feature.

Because of the interrelationship between adrenomedullary and adreno-cortical secretions, and the implication of cortisol in the adaptation to stress, the plasma cortisol response of the subjects under test was also examined.

Increased secretion of catecholamine by the adrenal medulla triggers the release of adrenocorticotropic hormone releasing factor by the pituitary, thence ACTH which in turn stimulates the production of steroids – principally cortisol, by the adrenal cortex. Increased levels of corticosteroids have a potentiating effect on the enzyme responsible for the conversion of noradrenaline to adrenaline, completing the cycle.

The levels of cortisol secretion in the responsive group conformed to the previously reported pattern observed in normals in similar situations, there being a significant increase in mean plasma cortisol. However, the hyporesponsive group exhibited only a small change which was not statistically significant. The base values were, in each case, very similar (Woodman, Hinton and O'Neill, 1978b). Such a finding is not altogether surprising since the adrenaline levels of the hyporesponsive groups are so low. The cortisol response normally triggered off by the increased adrenaline secretion has obviously been greatly modified.

Surprisingly, levels of cyclic nucleotides, cyclic adenosine monophosphate and cyclic guanosine monophosphate which, broadly speaking, act as second messengers to adrenaline and noradrenaline respectively, were not greatly different. The responsive hospital group did show slightly higher urinary cyclic AMP levels than all the other groups but the hyporesponsive group showed similar cyclic AMP levels to the two control groups despite having a lower adrenaline output (Woodman and Hinton, 1978a). Cyclic GMP levels were similar in both security hospital groups despite the discrepancy in noradrenaline levels.

A number of unusual results have therefore been obtained in this study so far, the principal one being the abnormal catecholamine balance in the physiologically hyporesponsive patients. These abnormalities cannot be attributed to the strictures of institutional confinement, since both the responsive security patient group and the mentally ill control group are similarly confined but have results similar to the normal group who are not confined.

There is therefore good reason to believe that the altered response is genuine and a function of the individual rather than the setting. It is also pertinent that out of a total of 115 control and test subjects studied, the abnormal catecholamine ratio was only seen in patients confined in the maximum security hospital.

This catecholamine imbalance might well have a direct bearing on the periodic antisocial violent behaviour of these patients. From previous work, it appears that increases in noradrenaline relative to adrenaline might possibly be interpreted emotionally as feelings of aggression, but that adrenaline increase relative to noradrenaline would normally be expected to produce anxiety or apprehension. The physiologically hyporesponsive patients show both a lack of the normal adrenaline response and exhibit an enhanced production of noradrenaline in stressful situations. Thus the indication is that lack of normal catecholamine responses might relate to a failure of these patients to experience anxiety.

The interpretation of the possible emotional manipulation resulting from the unusually high secretion of noradrenaline is less sure. The connection between high noradrenaline secretion and aggression previously claimed by a number of workers invites speculation that this excess might predispose the individual to feelings of an aggressive nature. At the very least, it seems reasonable to anticipate that these individuals with high noradrenaline would lack the restraining influence of anticipatory fear which would render their previous case histories a little more explicable. None of the patients undergoing the testing programme exhibited overt aggressive behaviour during the test period; the attitude of many of the patients with high NA/A ratio appeared to be one of 'easy-going' unconcern.

This could be taken as evidence supporting the work of Levi (1972) and Frankenhaeuser (1971) that adrenaline is responsible for the intensity of emotional reaction, and that the type of reaction is the product of a variety of cognitive and environmental factors, noradrenaline having little influence on the process.

The reactions noted, however, were elicited by fairly moderate stressors and it could be argued that if such conditions produce a shift from the anxious end of the mood spectrum, then more severe conditions, proscribed by experimental ethics but encountered in the day-to-day life of these patients, might produce a further shift towards feelings of aggression or anger. It is tempting to extend this possibility and compare the degree of violence in the subject's history to the catecholamine balance during stress anticipation. Taking convicted crimes as the criterion, by far the more violent group are the psychophysiologically hyporesponsive group of patients who show the highest noradrenaline to adrenaline ratios.

Although this group itself accounted for only 24 per cent of the security hospital sample, it contained 57 per cent of the patients convicted of crimes resulting in fatality. This apparent predisposition to killing in the hyporesponsive group is compounded with a high incidence of attacks on strangers. Sixty-four per cent of the victims of this group were unknown to the offender compared with 20 per cent in the responsive group.

So, in addition to the biochemically abnormal apprehension response, this group of patients also exhibited a low physiological anxiety type responsivity to stress, most notably in the responses of neuromuscular and cardiovascular systems, and a history of convictions for extreme personal physical violence. These characteristics agree closely with primary psychopathy theory. Furthermore, the observation that an abnormally high noradrenaline to adrenaline ratio tended to differentiate the most physically violent patients from the rest to a greater extent during the period of anticipation of the stress-testing programme is consistent with the view that conditioned anticipatory fear is deficient in psychopathic personalities (Trasler, 1962).

It can be seen from Figure 8.2 that there is a tendency for subjects with convictions only for violent crimes to have a higher noradrenaline to adrenaline ratio than either those subjects with a mixed violence and property crime background or those with convictions for sexual offences. This again bears out the theories that increased noradrenaline production relative to adrenaline production is found in more aggressive personalities. These correlations raise interesting and provocative questions. First of all, is there a reasonable biochemical explanation of the abnormal response and its apparent permanence in the physiologically hyporesponsive group of patients? Two possibilities seem to exist: first, the brain can promote the preferential production of either adrenaline or noradrenaline by nervous stimulation emanating from specific brain areas, so the abnormality could be a result of the brain providing a faulty stimulus. However, this would not necessarily account for the simultaneous decrease in adrenaline.

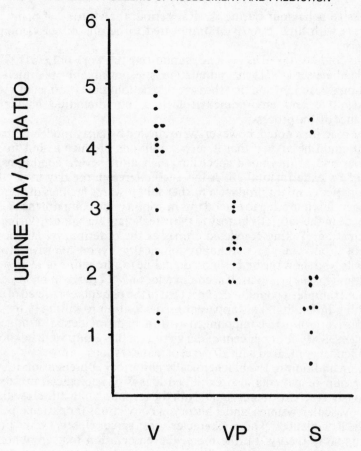

Figure 8.2 *Urine noradrenaline to adrenaline ratio during a period of anticipation in physiologically responsive subjects with convictions for violence alone (V), mixed violence and property offences (VP) and sexual offences (S).*

The second possibility is therefore more attractive, that is, that a defect exists in the process controlling the conversion of noradrenaline to adrenaline. This would allow the normal biochemical response to take place up to the point where noradrenaline is converted to adrenaline but the step would not be completed, resulting in the high noradrenaline outflow in situations normally characterised by adrenaline release.

Bearing these factors in mind, it is interesting to look at some recent animal work. It has been repeatedly shown that individually housed mice develop significantly more aggressive characteristics than group-house mice (Welch and Welch, 1971). When newborn mice removed from the mother and isolated for approximately four weeks are brought together, spontaneous fighting occurs. Concurrently the mice also develop a permanently impaired ability to synthesise the enzyme responsible for converting noradrenaline to adrenaline (Axelrod *et al.*, 1970).

This raises the possibility that the antisocial aggression produced by isolation is associated with the relative increase in noradrenaline. Additionally it has been shown that children raised under more deprived conditions and subjected to harsher parental discipline develop a higher noradrenaline to adrenaline ratio. These factors point to the possibility that certain behavioural characteristics which are moulded by the environment obtain a high degree of permanence by the fundamental modification of biochemical systems and that the action taken by an individual to any threatening situation will largely depend on how his total past experience has implanted itself on to his basic biochemical processes. So in an already aggressive personality, it would appear that this characteristic could be enhanced by certain environmental conditions.

While this study has concentrated on the biochemical aberrations encountered in adrenal secretions during the stress anticipation response, there are definite indications that changes in prolactin secretion and an altered habituation response (Woodman, 1979b) occur in our abnormal subjects. Much work obviously remains to be done, since the studies described have all been of a fairly restricted and short-term nature. However, there are definite points which offer interesting long-term possibilities.

The case record data is inevitably incomplete, so correlations with biological data must be made with caution. Nevertheless, one cannot ignore the finding that, compared with the group showing normal stress responses, the group showing abnormal stress responses exhibits a much higher percentage of crimes involving fatal outcome and physical attacks on strangers.

In general terms, it is well recognised that established behavioural characteristics tend to remain fairly constant, and an individual's future behaviour can be reasonably accurately assessed from knowledge of his past behaviour. More pertinent from our point of view, a recent study by Black (1977) on records of past maximum security hospital detainees has suggested that the best indicator of future offending is previous record, especially previous convictions for attacks on strangers.

At this time, these studies cannot offer any predictive aspect, but the possibility of a predictive biological dimension has to be acknowledged.

The work described offers no easy answers, but the findings cannot be lightly dismissed. Biochemical and psychophysiological studies of behavioural abnormalities in maximum security hospital patients deserve a much fuller, long-term appraisal, for should such abnormal responses prove to be consistent, permanent features, the possibility arises that the availability of quantifiable, unfakeable biological parameters could result in a significant improvement in the assessment of an individual's potential dangerousness, making reintegration of offenders into the community both safer and therefore more acceptable to the public at large.

9 Social Construing and Violent Behaviour in Mentally Abnormal Offenders

KEVIN HOWELLS

The work to be reported in this chapter arose out of attempts to understand the phenomenology of the 'dangerous' offender. The work began in a period in which the author practised as a clinical psychologist on the Admission Ward of one of the English Special Hospitals. My main task at that time was to interview and assess newly admitted patients. These (male) patients had been defined as 'mentally abnormal' and the vast majority had been recently convicted of violent offences against the person. The main focus of my conversations with the patients was to achieve some understanding of the subjective context of the person's violent behaviour, to assess how he[1] had constructed reality before, and at the time of, the violent incident, how he had perceived himself, his circumstances, significant others in his life and, in particular, his victim. Typically, having tried to reconstruct the past, we would move to how he saw the present and his future. These attempts to elucidate private perceptions were informed and facilitated by some aspects of personal construct theory (Kelly, 1955) and of attribution theory (Jones et al., 1971) and often involved the administration of some form of repertory grid (Fransella and Bannister, 1977). Subsequent to these exploratory efforts it became possible to administer grids and other measures in a standardised manner in a formal research context over several years. The data from this later work form the basis of the results to be reported below.

The Relevance of Cognitive Processes

The relevance of epistemological or cognitive processes to a wide range of types of social difficulty has been increasingly recognised in recent years. This recognition stems, in part, from developments in the field of attribution theory within experimental social psychology (for example, Valins and Nisbett, 1971; Storms and McCaul, 1976) and from progress in the clinical application of personal construct theory (for example, Fransella, 1972) and cognitive therapy (Beck, 1979). Workers within all of these fields have stressed the necessity to understand how persons represent and explain reality and how such representations determine normal and abnormal behaviour. Although aggressive and violent behaviour has received much less attention than states such as anxiety and depression there is now good reason to believe that how a person appraises and construes people and events is an important determinant of whether or not he will behave violently.

The most comprehensive analysis of the role of cognitive structuring in the genesis of anger and ensuing aggression has been provided by Novaco (1978). Within Novaco's model, anger (which often, though not invariably, induces aggression) is a product of particular modes of appraisal of aversive (frustrating) situations and people – 'aversive events function as provocations because of the way they are construed' (1978, pp. 141–2). A number of such violence-engendering modes of appraisal have been described, including the attribution of malevolent intent (Epstein and Taylor, 1967; Greenwell and Dengerink, 1973; Nickel, 1974) and paranoid social cognitions (Howells, 1981b). Further evidence for the relevance of appraisal for violent behaviour can be found in a recent symbolic interactionist account of violent incidents (Athens, 1980) which focuses attention on the situation confronting the violent person, his interpretation and definition of that situation and on the planning and execution of the violent act. This study, although open to a number of methodological criticisms, provides an unusually fine-grained account of the phenomenology of the violent situation for the person and concludes that 'violent actors do form interpretations of the situations in which they commit violent acts' and that 'the interpretations they form ... account for the violent actions'.

Repertory Grid Studies

Studies stemming from personal construct theory are infrequent in the field of violent offending and 'dangerous' behaviour, despite the clear relevance of this theoretical framework for understanding the subjective world of the violent person. A small number of studies have, however, used repertory grids to assess personal construing in offender groups. Lewis (1973) investigated construing in a sample of British prisoners and found changes in self-construing over time in long-term prisoners. Topcu (1976) found aggressive psychiatric patients to differ from controls on some aspects of appraisal of self, and Norris (1977) described a number of changes in the construction of ideal self in young men sentenced to detention centres. None of these studies, however, could be said to have focused on the dangerously violent offender. A handful of studies have investigated this latter group. Widom (1976) investigated personal construing in samples of psychopathic violent offenders confined in a Special Hospital and demonstrated that violent 'primary psychopaths' failed to acknowledge the discrepancies that existed between their own constructions of situations and the constructions of the same situations by other people. These results provide some support for Gough's thesis (1948) that the central deficiency in psychopathy is one of undeveloped role-taking.

In recent years the current author has reported some repertory grid work with offenders typically perceived as dangerous. In a study of rapists (Howells and Steadman-Allen, 1977), repertory grids were used to explore rapists' definitions of their emotional state at the time of the rape incident, in order to clarify whether they perceived themselves as aggressively or sexually aroused. A study of a small sample of pedophilic offenders (Howells, 1979a) demonstrated that pedophiles' attraction to children was partly a function of their unusual personal construing of adults and that their construct systems differed in content from those of controls. It is the opinion of the author, however, that the main usefulness of grid technique lies in the detailed elucidation of the intrapersonal world of the violent *individual* rather than in group studies. One of the major problems confronting the Special Hospitals and other agencies and institutions concerned with the management of the 'dangerous' offender is the assessment of a very small group of offenders whose motivation is unclear and apparently bizarre. At the time of writing, for example, there has been considerable discussion within the British mass media as to the motivation of the 'Yorkshire Ripper' who was assumed to have been responsible and was subsequently committed for a series of murderous assaults on women. In such cases the extremity of the violent behaviour observed, and its apparent repetitive nature, are such that the average citizen, and even the psychologist or psychiatrist, finds it difficult to understand the violent behaviour in terms of recognisable motives and states of mind. Whereas an explosively angry impulsive assault can, perhaps, be related to and understood in terms of our own past experiences of intense anger, repetitive, apparently planned, violence may appear entirely incomprehensible. Such offenders pose a problem for assessment, prediction and treatment efforts. When the offender's cognitive framework and motives are inaccessible in this way, it becomes correspondingly difficult to predict whether, and in what circumstances, he may re-offend and to offer appropriate help to the offender himself. A small number of offenders of this sort account for a substantial proportion of the difficult decisions to be made by mental health and judicial personnel. A repertory grid investigation can sometimes provide insights in such cases which are not easily obtained by other means. By way of illustration of this, the author (Howells, 1979b) has reported in detail on the construct system of a man admitted to a hospital following attempts to poison others. The study confirmed that deviant behaviour, in this case, was associated with an 'alternative definition of social reality' – a definition which it would be extremely difficult to appreciate through other means of assessment.

Overcontrol in Violent Offenders

Later in this chapter I shall be reporting some repertory grid results from work with 'overcontrolled' violent offenders. I propose to briefly review the history of the notion as a preliminary to reporting my own work.

Many studies of offenders convicted of acts of extreme violence, such as homicide, have provided paradoxical results. The paradox has been that the intensity and severity of violence have shown a *positive* correlation with personality measures of control and low hostility. Megargee observed (1966, 1971) that many persons who commit extreme assaults do not conform to the popular stereotype of the violent offender, being characterised by traits of social inhibitedness, low assertiveness and denial of anger rather than by impulsive aggressiveness. These observations have been explained by Megargee in terms of a theory of overcontrol which states, briefly, that some people may be excessively inhibited about the expression of anger and hostility and that such persons, in certain circumstances, may summate frustration over a long period of time until their threshold of inhibition is exceeded and an explosive and excessively violent act is precipitated. In early work (1966) Megargee provided some empirical evidence that extremely assaultive (EA) juvenile delinquents obtained lower scores than moderately assaultive (MA) delinquents on 22 out of 28 aggression scores derived from psychometric tests. The EA group was found to have the higher percentage of first offenders and to have the better school conduct and attendance record. Molof (1967) found that delinquent boys convicted of serious assaults (equated by Megargee (1971) with his EA group) had a more favourable family background and a history suggesting better socialisation.

There have been a number of replications of Megargee's work, a sample of which will be discussed here. Blackburn (1968) compared EA and MA groups selected from admissions to an English Special Hospital and predicted that EAs would score higher on measures of control, conformity and denial, and lower on measures of hostility and impulsivity. All measures were derived from the MMPI item pool. Predictions were confirmed for most measures and particularly for measures of impulsivity/control. Blackburn found that 82 per cent of the EA group had attacked known victims (family, friends, neighbours) whilst only 36 per cent of the MA group knew their victims. This is consistent with Megargee's notion that the overcontrolled aggressor needs prolonged and sustained frustration in order for his inhibitions to be exceeded. Subsequently the same author (Blackburn, 1971) used a clustering technique to create types amongst a sample of British homicides and identified two of the four types revealed as indicating overcontrol. More recent studies have provided further validation (Arnold and Quinsey, 1977; Widom, 1978; McGurk, 1978) though some studies have failed to replicate the early findings (Crawford, 1977). The study of McGurk and McGurk (1979) raises some doubts about the meaning of profiles supposedly indicating overcontrol. In this study overcontrolled profiles were found to be common amongst non-violent prisoners and also amongst 'normal' controls (prison officers). In fact, in this study, more than 70 per cent of the prison officer sample were classified as overcontrolled. This finding would seem to suggest that 'controlled' is a more appropriate epithet to describe such profiles when they occur amongst violent offenders, and also raises the possibility that the observed greater control in violent groups is a function of an above average level of 'undercontrolled' traits in comparison groups (for example, non-violent prisoners).

Megargee's model, and the data presented as supporting it, are weak in several respects. Some possible criticisms have been discussed elsewhere (Howells, 1981b). One major difficulty is that research in this area has been dominated by the MMPI, and similar tests, which are ill suited to the assessment of personality variables relating to control and hostility, and which may be highly susceptible to the effects of extreme test-taking response sets induced by the unusual social context of testing sessions (for example, that of admission to a prison or security hospital following homicide). Such situations are likely, perhaps, to produce reactions in the subject of either extreme denial or extreme over-endorsement of problems. It is not inconceivable that overcontrolled and other profiles observed in such contexts are a product of such response sets. There is, therefore, a clear need to study overcontrolled groups on measures other than the traditionally psychometric. An attempt to use repertory grids for this purpose will be reported below.

A Study of Construing in Abnormal Offenders

The repertory grid work to be reported was completed mainly within one of the Special Hospitals in England and Wales. The persons studied consisted of 106 male patients admitted to the hospital and twenty-four male prisoners confined to a prison in the south of England. For the Special Hospital group the majority had convictions for violent offences, including murder, manslaughter, wounding and assaults. A small number had been admitted to the hospital following violent episodes in other psychiatric hospitals, but without a court conviction. All the patient group had been deemed to be suffering from a mental abnormality, as defined by the 1959 Mental Health Act. Approximately half of this group had been admitted under the 'mental illness' classification of the Act and half under the 'psychopathic disorder' classification. The prisoner group was recruited from non-aggressive offenders admitted to an industrial prison. Previous studies by prison psychologists had demonstrated that the population of the prison was comparable to the prison population in general, in terms of personality characteristics, social class and IQ level. The prison group was selected from recent receptions, having excluded prisoners beginning a sentence of less than three years and prisoners with any recorded offence involving violence or sexual assault. The remaining prisoners consisted of men with convictions for offences of an acquisitive rather than aggressive nature. The prison group was selected to produce a group with similar distributions of age, social class and verbal IQ to the Special Hospital group.

Determination of Comparison Groups

The Special Hospital group was subdivided on the basis of criminal history. A criminal history was obtained for each patient and the number and type of previous convictions were recorded. Twenty-nine patients were found to have no convictions previous to the current violent offence ('one-off' offenders). Seventy-seven patients had previous convictions. Virtually all the patients in the latter group ('multiple' offenders) had previous convictions of more than one type, including violent, acquisitive and sexual offences. The one-off offenders had aggressed primarily against their families or close acquaintances (89.5 per cent) and many of the victims had died (44.9 per cent). The multiple offenders were less likely to have attacked family or close acquaintances (32.5 per cent) and fewer victims had died (13 per cent). Independent judges rated the violence of the current offence as significantly more extreme in the one-off than in the multiple offender group. These figures suggest that the two groups had much similarity to the 'extreme' and 'moderate' assault groups studied by Blackburn (1968). The one-off aggressors had a mean age of 31 and a mean verbal IQ of 107, the multiple aggressors a mean age of 27 and mean verbal IQ of 103, and the non-aggressive prisoners a mean age of 26 and a mean verbal IQ of 105. The ranges and standard deviations of scores were similar for all groups. The subjects selected are taken by the author as defining three groups for comparison: one-off extremely assaultive aggressors (over-controlled), multiple moderately assaultive aggressors (undercontrolled), and non-aggressive controls.

Procedure

The vast majority of the hospital group were tested within a few months of admission, a small number being tested in the course of referrals for assessment to the psychology department. All the non-aggressive prisoners were tested shortly after reception. Each subject completed a Role Construct Repertory Grid administered by the self-identification method (Kelly, 1955). Subjects were required to name eighteen people to fit a standard role-title list which included parents, family and authority figures and aspects of self. The three self elements included were 'Myself as I am' (actual self), 'Myself as I would like to be' (ideal self) and 'Myself as others see me' (social self). Fifteen bi-polar constructs were elicited on a 5-point scale with 3 as a mid-point. The grid took between $1\frac{1}{2}$ and 2 hours to complete. The matrix of ratings (18 elements × 15 constructs) was submitted to Slater's Ingrid Analysis (Slater, 1972, 1976, 1977). This programme describes the construct/element variance in terms of the principal components and also describes the 'distance' between all elements. The content of elicited constructs was also investigated using a reliable categorisation system devised by the author.

Group Comparison Measures

Repertory grid technique is an essentially idiographic method, suited to the analysis of the individual case. The Ingrid analysis does, however, allow group comparisons on particular measures. The following scores were selected from individual analyses as being relevant to the assessment of hostility and control in the three groups:

(1)   The 'actual self'–'ideal self' distance.
(2)   The 'social self'–'ideal self' distance.
      (Both these measures assess aspects of self-dissatisfaction and intro-punitivesness.)
(3)   The number of non-self elements whose distance from ideal self was smaller than the distance of actual self from ideal self. This might be

regarded as a measure of intropunitive/extrapunitive balance, assessing whether the subject views himself more positively or more negatively than he views other persons in his life.

(4)   The relative salience of positive and negative evaluation poles in construct elicitation. For some individuals, when comparing elements, 'positive' features of elements are salient ('friendly', 'sympathetic', 'nice') and are the poles that are elicited first. Negative features ('unfriendly', 'cold', 'nasty') are only elicited as the contrasts (see Adams-Webber, 1979). Pilot work demonstrated that independent judges showed good agreement as to which was the 'good' and which the 'bad' pole of constructs. For each subject in the current study, each construct pole was rated by judges, and the pole elicited first was defined as either the positive evaluation or negative evaluation pole. The measure was defined as the number of positive poles elicited first divided by the number of negative poles elicited first.

(5)   The Bias and Variability measures of response set (Slater, 1972, 1977). These are measures of the tendencies to rate all elements towards one pole, and to restrict element ratings to a position near the mean respectively. Pilot work demonstrated that high Bias scores reflected a tendency to rate all elements positively, that is, as lying at the 'good' pole of the constructs. (See Adams-Webber, ch. 7, for a discussion of lopsidedness in construing.) Both these measures might be regarded as measuring control in the evaluation of elements.

In addition to the measures described, the percentage of construct variation accounted for by the first principal component was assessed for each grid. This is widely used as a measure of cognitive simplicity (Fransella and Bannister, 1977). Topcu (1976) reported an association of cognitive simplicity, as assessed by this measure, and violence in psychiatric patients.

It was predicted that the overcontrolled group (one-off offenders) would show indications of more control, more bias towards positivity, less criticism of others and more criticism of self in construing, on the measures described, than the comparison groups. Specifically, the overcontrolled offenders would demonstrate more bias, less variability, be more likely to elicit positive poles first, perceive more non-self elements as closer to ideal self and perceive a greater distance between actual and ideal self and social and ideal self. No specific predictions were made with regard to the first component measure.

Results

As grids are meant to elicit *personal* construing, two individual grids will be reported first, to demonstrate, briefly, the range of types of construct systems found, and the possible clinical utility of the data. Both these grids are of particular interest in that they include the victim of the current assault amongst the elements. More general features of victim evaluation will be discussed below.

Figure 9.1 shows the plot of a sample of significant elements on the first two principal components of the grid (Slater, 1972, 1977) for a Special Hospital patient. The subject in this case was a black African convicted of an assault on one of his employers, in the context of what appeared to be paranoid delusional beliefs about his employers generally. The horizontal axis represents the first principal component, the vertical axis the second. The constructs defining the components are shown. The constructs for each component are significantly intercorrelated. The first component relates to respect and the absence of racial prejudice (associated with being black). The second component relates to honesty and trustworthiness. The overall plot suggests that the employers ('victim' and 'other boss') are/were resented for what was perceived as a lack of respect, a tendency to prejudice, and untrustworthiness. Actual and ideal self can be seen to be relatively close, though actual self is perceived as 'too honest for my own good'. It can be seen that such a map of person perceptions suggests, in this case, a number of hypotheses as to why the assault occurred and how it related to the person's central concerns and core constructs. It might be hypothesised, for example, that the offence had been precipitated by feelings of resentment about the way he had been treated by his employers, and that some of this resentment related to a sense of being a victim of racial prejudice.

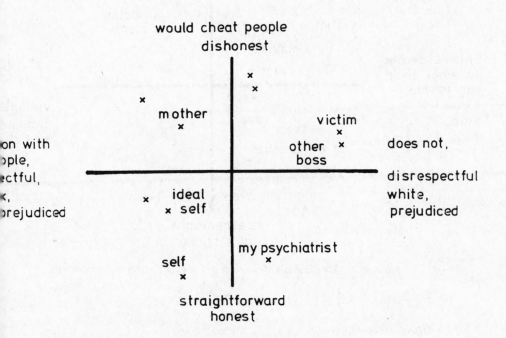

Figure 9.1 *Plot of sample of elements on principal components: individual 1. (Elements not central to the discussion have been left unlabelled.)*

Figure 9.2 shows a very different cognitive system. These results are from the grid of a young man who killed his girlfriend. Clinical assessments had shed little light on the motive for and feelings preceding the violent assault. The person himself admitted to little hostility, either currently or in the past, towards his victim, and, apparently, found it difficult to explain to himself why the assault occurred. The first component in this case is defined by constructs relating to being understood and helpful, and the second by constructs relating to respectability (which has negative connotations). Actual and ideal self are, again, closely aligned. The victim is clearly very positively evaluated on the first component, providing a marked contrast with Figure 9.1, though there is mild dislike of the victim on component 2. One of the most interesting features of this particular system is the very negative evaluation of the victim's mother, a finding which would clearly need to be explored in more detail in determining the motive for the offence.

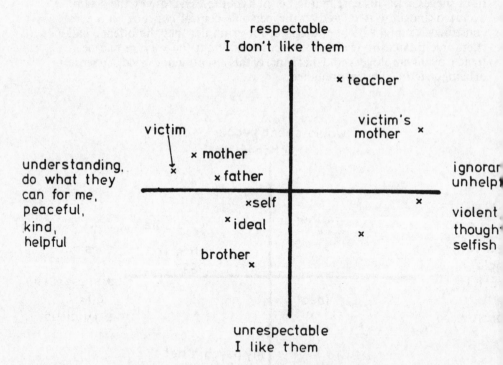

Figure 9.2   *Plot of sample of elements on principal components: individual 2.*

Group Results

There was no significant correlation between either age or verbal IQ and any group measure. The data for the three subject groups were submitted to a one-way analysis of variance. The overall F-ratio was significant for actual–ideal self distance ($p < 0.01$) and the positive/negative elicited poles measure ($p < 0.01$) but not for the other measures. As planned comparisons were made it was permissible to proceed to analysis of the difference between specific groups, even when the three group F-ratio was insignificant. Table 9.1 shows the group means and Table 9.2 the probabilities for group comparisons.

Table 9.1   *Means for Group Measures*

Measure	Mean one-off overcontrolled (N=29)	Mean multiple undercontrolled (N=77)	Mean non-aggressive prisoners (N=24)
Actual–ideal self distance	0·902	0·721	0·721
Social–ideal self distance	0·862	0·807	0·756
Non-self elements closer to ideal	8·04	5·69	5·83
Positive/negative poles first	6·73	3·93	2·79
Bias	0·423	0·380	0·343
Variability	0·608	0·643	0·684
1st component	55·5	51·5	48·4

Table 9.2   *Significance Levels (Two-Tailed) for Differences between Groups*

Measure	One-off versus prisoners	One-off versus multiple	One-off versus combined prisoners and multiple
Actual–ideal self distance	$p < 0.01$	$p < 0.01$	$p < 0.01$
Social–ideal self distance	n.s.	n.s.	n.s.
Non-self elements closer to ideal	n.s.	$p < 0.05$	$p < 0.05$
Positive/negative poles first	$p < 0.01$	$p < 0.01$	$p < 0.01$
Bias	$p < 0.05$	n.s.	n.s.
Variability	n.s.	n.s.	n.s.
1st component	n.s.	n.s.	n.s.

It can be seen from the tables that the overcontrolled group's means are in the predicted direction on all measures, though some fail to reach significance. The one-off group is significantly more dissatisfied with actual self, though not with social self. The one-off group compare themselves significantly more negatively with others and are markedly more prone to elicit a positively evaluated construct pole first. The one-off group elicit almost seven times more positive than negative poles first, as compared to an average of three times in the control groups. The one-off offenders produce more biased grids (significantly so when compared with the non-aggressive prisoners). There are no significant group differences for variability and the first component measure.

Construct Content

An analysis of construct content in the three groups provided few significant differences. The one significant finding was that one-off aggressive offenders were less likely to use constructs concerning obedience/non-obedience to the law (for example, criminal ... law abiding, a thief ... honest). The most plausible interpretation of this finding is that it reflects the failure of the generally conforming one-off offender to incorporate criminal subculture. The one-off offender has committed only one (although extreme) criminal act, and a criminal career has not, in the past, been one of his options. It is unlikely that he will view criminality as a potential future role in the same way that the multiple aggressive offender or the non-aggressive prisoner might. It is important to remember, though, that the fact that the multiple offenders and the prisoners use criminality constructs more often does not necessarily imply that they identify with the 'criminal' rather than the 'non-criminal' pole. Informal inspection of the position of these constructs within individual construct systems suggested that these offenders were evenly divided between those who identified with the criminal pole and those who did not.

Construing of Victims

The victims of the current assault often appeared amongst the elements provided for the role titles, as the victim was often the wife, girlfriend, mother, father, or some other intimate acquaintance of the offender. A small sub-sample of the aggressive patients were asked to include the victim somewhere in the element list if he/she did not already appear. This provided a total sample of thirty-five victims whose location within construct systems could be evaluated. The relationship of the victim to the offender was as follows: wife or current girlfriend – 13 cases; father – 5 cases; mother – 6 cases; brother – 1 case; other acquaintances – 10. All of the victims were sufficiently known to the offender to enable him to report judgements of the victim on the grid.

Individual analyses of victim perceptions indicated considerable individual variation in how victims were perceived. In some systems victims were viewed in an obviously hostile manner (see Figure 9.1) and in others in a positive and even idealised, way (see Figure 9.2). Initial inspection suggested that positive evaluations were more frequent in the one-off extreme assault group than in the multiple offender group. In this particular sample of victims all of the sixteen victims of the one-off group had died as a result of the assault, but the nineteen victims of the multiple assault group had survived. It was possible to compare the evaluation of dead and surviving victims in terms of the conceptual distances (Slater, 1972, 1977) between the victim and other elements. This analysis showed that the rank order of element distances from victims was very different for the two groups. Dead victims were seen, for example, as significantly closer to actual self ($p < 0.01$), closer to ideal self ($p < 0.01$) and more distant from the element 'A person who annoys me' ($p < 0.02$) than were surviving victims. In general, the (dead) victims of serious assaults were typically construed in a positive way, often appearing as the most positively evaluated person within the grid. This was much less true for the (surviving) victims of the less serious assaults. Dead victims who had been the wives of the assailants were particularly likely to be evaluated in a highly positive manner. This is illustrated in Figure 9.3 which shows the conceptual distance of wife and other sorts of victim from the elements 'actual self' and 'a person I really disliked'. Wife victims were significantly more positively evaluated than parent and other victims on a variety of element distance measures, and were more positively evaluated than a control group of non-victim wives.

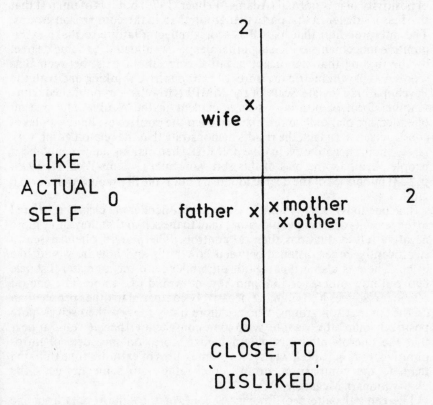

Figure 9.3   *Mean distances of different victim types from concepts of 'actual self' and 'a person I really dislike'.*

The analysis of whether victims tended to be given extreme ratings on *particular* constructs proved disappointing. The aggressive offenders were idiosyncratic in terms of which constructs differentiated victims. For one offender the victim might be seen as 'immoral', for another as 'cold and indifferent', for another as 'authoritarian', little consistency across subjects being found, thus endorsing the view that grids require individual analysis.

Discussion

The overall pattern of results does suggest that the one-off extremely assaultive offenders differ in their personal construing from the multiple moderately assaultive offenders and from non-aggressive prisoners. The one-off offenders show more control in their judgements about people (as measured by Bias and Variability) though only the comparison with non-aggressive prisoners on Bias attains statistical significance. The high Bias score indicates that the one-off offenders tend to refer elements to one pole (in this case the positive evaluation pole) of their constructs. Some degree of positivity bias is normal (Adams-Webber, 1979) but it is of interest that this bias is greater in this particular group than in the comparison groups. The interpretation that high Bias scores reflect a failure to make extra-punitive judgements criticising other people is validated, to some degree, by the finding that significant negative correlations exist between Bias scores and psychometric measures of extrapunitive thinking and with the Psychopathic Deviate Scale of the MMPI (Howells – unpublished data). Another form of positivity bias is evident in the results. The one-off offenders are markedly more likely to elicit the positive evaluative poles of constructs first. In fact, the results demonstrate that the one-off group very rarely elicit a negative evaluative pole first when making judgements about people. Again, some bias of this sort is normal (Adams-Webber, 1979, p. 173) but biases of the degree found are not typically reported in normal groups.

The positivity biases found in the one-off offender are clearly restricted to judgements of other people rather than to the self in that they show more negative self-evaluations than do controls. The one-off offender sees a significantly larger distance between how he is and how he would like to be. There is also a non-significant tendency to see a greater distance between how others see him and how he would like to be. The one-off offender also sees himself more negatively compared to other people than do the comparison groups, who are more likely to view themselves more positively than other people. With some consistency, then, it would appear that the one-off offenders obtain higher scores on measures of intro-punitive thinking and lower scores on measures of extrapunitive thinking than do the comparison groups, confirming – to some degree – the observations of Megargee.

The general pattern of findings is confirmed by the results from the victim evaluation study. Paradoxically, again, the one-off offenders, who had committed the most extreme assaults, leading to the death of their victims, rated their victims in a more positive and idealised way than did the comparison group, who were more likely to perceive victims in a hostile manner. These positive evaluations of dead victims are most marked for wives killed by the testees, and are unrealistically positive in so far as the ratings of these wives are more positive and idealised than the ratings of wives by controls, who had not assaulted their wives. It is possible, of course, that idealised evaluations of victims (and biased construct systems in general) are *reactions* to the offence rather than reflections of attitudes which existed prior to the offence. This criticism applies to all psychological studies which, inevitably, can only assess the offender after the violent act has occurred.

If we make the assumption that the biases in personal construing found in this study did exist prior to the offence and were long-term features of offenders' perceptual systems, what would they suggest about the interpersonal perceptions of the one-off offender and the changes preceding the explosive violent assault?

The significant tendency of one-off offenders to find the positive features of persons more salient would seem to relate to conventional notions of low hostility. Such a tendency could be indicative of a 'repressive' or 'overcontrolled' mode of social perception. One-off offenders could be seen as constructing a social reality in which the positive features of other people's behaviour are the most salient and in which 'bad' features are the implicit and 'submerged' poles of their constructs. Such a person would live in a world in which he perceived only evidence of people's niceness and friendliness, until his perceptual system was undermined. Kelly (1955) has discussed how one end of a construct may be less available to the person than the other. The non-available end he refers to as 'submerged', and suggests that submerged poles tend to be the *contrast* poles, that is, the poles elicited second. It is central to construct theory that constructs are bi-polar , that one cannot refer to the likeness aspect of the construct without simultaneously evoking the difference aspect of the construct. Within such a framework, the consistent submerging of one pole of a construct (as in one-off offenders) would be an indication of a disordered and rather vulnerable construct system. Kelly suggests that submergence may be a handy way of keeping a construct from being tested: 'Perhaps the client fears that, if the submerged end of a construct is uncovered, he will have to reconstrue himself, with far reaching and devastating consequences' (Kelly, 1955). Kelly's example of this is particularly relevant to the one-off offenders being studied. He suggests that, for example, a person may maintain the construct 'everyone is nice' at considerable cost to himself as a desperate effort to keep from construing himself as a person who has been badly treated. Kelly points out (p. 235) that if the constructs 'Nice' and 'Gentle', to which 'Aggressive' or 'Nasty' are the contrasting poles, begin to break down under extremely stressful circumstances, the subject may turn to 'Aggressive' and 'Nasty' both as a way of seeing other people and as a way of behaving himself. It might be suggested that the one-off offender finds it increasingly difficult to maintain his idealised view of other people (and of his victim) when faced with severe interpersonal difficulties, until a point is reached where his system breaks downs. Violence may occur at either of two points: (1) in the situation of 'threat' preceding the final breakdown (Kelly defines threat as 'the awareness of imminent comprehensive change in one's core constructs'). At this stage a particular person (that is, the subsequent victim) may become the source of threat, and, in some sense, need to be 'obliterated'; (2) in the confused state following the invalidation of established constructions, a dramatic shift is made to the submerged poles of the person's constructs, so that, suddenly, others are seen in very negative, even paranoid terms, and this new perception 'legitimises' some form of violent reaction to them. These negative evaluations are temporary, and the offender subsequently reverts to his repressive evaluations of his victim and others. At the time of assessment in a Special Hospital the repressive mode of perception again predominates. This sort of view of the overcontrolled aggressor has many similarities to that propounded by Megargee, but locates the important change as being in the cognitive appraisal of the world by the offender rather than in some physiological build up of frustration. Both theories would suggest an appropriate therapy as being the attempt to break down excessive inhibitions about hostility. Within a Kellian framework, the submerged poles of the person's constructs would need to be brought to his attention. He would need to be gradually encouraged to explore the feelings and reactions he might have if he entertained a more hostile appraisal of the world. Such attempts would almost certainly meet initial reluctance and denial ('I never feel angry'; 'there is no one I dislike'; 'I never get resentful') and would require some skill if the person is not to feel overly threatened.

Summary and Conclusions

'Dangerous' violent behaviour cannot be understood and properly assessed without reference to the interpretive schema and the cognitive framework which the offender brings to bear on situations and people in his life. Until recently such epistemological variables have been neglected in research, assessment and treatment efforts in the field of violent behaviour. The work reported in this chapter amounts to a preliminary attempt to investigate some limited aspects of construing in mentally abnormal violent offenders using grid technique. Grids have been found in this study to provide a rich and detailed description of the individual case. Such descriptions often suggest a number of hypotheses as to why a violent assault has occurred and what future events and perceptions might induce future violent behaviour. It is also encouraging that grids can provide data amenable to a more nomothetic analysis. The personal construing of one-off overcontrolled offenders as a group has been shown to be different from that of less controlled and non-aggressive deviants in a number of areas. The results have been interpreted as consistent with Megargee's observations. Finally, it has been hypothesised that overcontrolled offenders may tend to have unstable, biased construct systems in which negative evaluations are submerged, and that these systems may be susceptible to abrupt, short-term changes producing uncharacteristic violence in normally controlled persons.

Note

As all of the work described has been conducted with male offenders, and males predominate amongst violent offenders in general, he/him rather than she/her is used to describe individuals.

Acknowledgements

I would like to thank the patients and prisoners who participated in this study, the many consultants at Broadmoor Hospital who co-operated in my work, Patrick Slater for the use of Ingrid '72 and for advice, and Phil Feldman and Tony Black for their general support. The criminal histories were obtained in collaboration with Elizabeth Parker of the Special Hospitals Research Unit. The author was supported by research funding from the Small Grants Fund of DHSS during the period in which the data were collected.

Part Four

Future Prospects for Research and Prediction

10 Some Statistical Questions in the Prediction of Dangerous Offending

JOHN COPAS

The subject of statistics endeavours to study situations which exhibit variability and uncertainty. When a schoolboy learns arithmetic, he is used to his answers being judged as either right or wrong. Given the question 2 × 3 = ?, all will agree that the answer 6 is correct, fixed and in a sense absolute – no deviation from this figure could be entertained or considered to have any scientific meaning. But when the question is 'how tall is a man?' no such answer is possible; the only answer we can give is one couched in statistical terms, for example, by quoting an average, or some other aspect of the distribution of men's heights. To expect precise and clear-cut predictions in the study of dangerous offending is equally absurd. The unexplained variability in behavioural patterns and the uncertainty in the identification and measurement of predictive factors are inherent features of the problem, and little research of an empirical nature can be undertaken without at least some appeal to statistical principles and methods. A few of the statistical problems which arise in the prediction of dangerous offending are discussed in this chapter. Such problems are not, of course, unique to this particular field of study; statistics, as a mathematical discipline, transcends the details of any single application. But the fact that low correlations, a large number of predictive factors and a relatively small sample size are the rule rather than the exception makes the problems of fitting and assessing prediction equations unusually acute. Methods which have been tried and tested in the more exact sciences may no longer be useful, and a reappraisal of some of the conventional statistical techniques seems both necessary and worthwhile.

Although statistical questions of research design are not to be considered here, the need for a sensible and well-thought-out strategy in the design and implementation of a study is obvious. The quality of a prediction equation cannot be greater than that of the data on which it is based. Besides the problems of definition and of assessment, which are characteristic of all empirical studies in dangerousness, and which are taken up elsewhere in this book, a number of methodological questions of a more statistical nature will also arise. In resolving such questions, much will depend on the particular circumstances and constraints facing the researcher. The main guide is that common sense should prevail; that, for instance, when a particular comparison is of interest, the data should allow it to be made on a 'like with like' basis. If the average height of a group of boys in country A is greater than that of a group of girls in country B, no amount of sophisticated statistical analysis will tell whether we should attribute the difference in height to sex or to the country of origin. It would have been better to have achieved an approximate balance over the cross-classification of sex with country, and even better to have recorded the ages of all the children involved. But if the children were not properly sampled then the data are probably worthless. Trite though this example may seem, it is surprising how often research workers collect their data according to a design which may at first sight seem sensible, but which, on closer examination, turns out to preclude the answering of the very question which motivated the investigation in the first place.

A prediction equation can only be constructed in terms of the variables or factors measured in the data which, in turn, have to be defined in a clear and unambiguous way. Considerable thought is usually needed in identifying the important factors to be measured, and in setting up a protocol for the data collection. For example, is it better to have a large sample with a short follow-up period, or a smaller sample with a longer follow-up period? Again, much will depend on particular circumstances and constraints but, needless to say, once the scope of the data is determined, then that delimits the range of validity of any prediction equation that can be constructed.

It is worth emphasising that the fitting of a prediction equation should be regarded as the last, and not the only, stage of a statistical analysis. The importance of the first stage, namely, data reduction and description, is nearly always underestimated. Many empirical studies in dangerousness are of a somewhat speculative nature, and may obtain information on a large number of factors which may, or may not, turn out to be associated with offending. The high variability in such factors may render the data quite opaque; the message of the data will only begin to be revealed when they are summarised in terms of statistics such as averages and percentages. Imaginative use of the main tool of data analysis, pencil and graph paper (or its equivalent in computer graphics), will be well rewarded by an increased insight into the information contained in the data. The close scrutiny of frequency tables for a wide variety of cross-classifications may be time-consuming but is nearly always worthwhile. Of course, once the data is in machine readable form, the actual calculation of such tables is simply handled by a statistical package computer programme such as is available in nearly all computer installations. In most cases, a summary of the data in terms of tables and graphs will be adequate and informative, although occasionally more sophisticated descriptive methods such as factor analysis, cluster analysis and multidimensional scaling are useful. However, their usefulness is a matter of some controversy amongst statisticians, and the mathematical properties of such procedures are not always well understood. A useful reference for such methods is Maxwell (1977).

As far as the fitting of a prediction equation is concerned, one of the aims of the preliminary descriptive analysis is to identify those variables which may be useful as predictive factors. It is important to note that, as a prediction equation will generally be based on more than one factor, it is not only the effects of *individual* factors that are important but also the *simultaneous* effects of many such factors. Sometimes two factors will interact with each other in the sense that the influence of one will be moderated by the value of the other. An instance of this kind is discussed in Copas and Whiteley (1976). Here, the rate of relapse (defined as reconviction for an offence or readmission to a psychiatric institution within two years) of psychopaths after discharge from a therapeutic community is being predicted on the basis of information available at the time of admission. The data analysis in this study revealed a strong interaction between recidivism (conviction for more than one offence in the past) and previous admission to a psychiatric hospital. Previous admission *lowered* the rate of relapse for the recidivists but *increased* the rate of relapse for the non-recidivists. Thus, in this study, there is clear evidence that any sensible method for predicting relapse should allow for not only the individual effects of recidivism and previous admission, but also the differential effect between them. This can be done by either fitting separate prediction equations for the recidivists and the non-recidivists, or by adding a new artificial predictive factor whose value is influenced by both recidivism *and* previous admission. This latter method is used in Copas and Whiteley (1976) and the reader is referred to that paper for further details.

With the possible addition of one or two new variables of the kind just mentioned, the research worker will often be faced with an unmanageably large number of potential predictive factors. It is mathematically impossible to fit a prediction equation which uses more factors than there are subjects in the study and, in any case, it is most unlikely that all of these factors will be equally useful as predictors. Usually, a high proportion of their total predictive power will be contained in just a few of them, and so some selection from all of the available factors is inevitable. The traditional way of separating the 'signal' from the 'noise' in this set of factors is to use significance tests: association between each individual factor and re-offending (or whatever response is being predicted) is tested for significance and only those factors giving significant results are selected. Unfortunately, the propriety of this method in the context of prediction studies is open to very considerable doubt and, although significance tests give a useful guide, they should not be interpreted too literally. A technical difficulty is that the chance of obtaining at least one spurious or chance result increases rapidly as the number of simultaneous tests increases. A more fundamental difficulty is that significance and predictive power are two separate statistical concepts: a factor which appears useful in terms of the first concept may not be useful in terms of the second concept, and vice versa. An analogy is in the mode of decision-making adopted by most individuals and organisations. Decisions are usually made on the basis of both hard evidence and soft evidence. Hard evidence, in the form of facts and figures, is open to scientific scrutiny and is likened to a statistically significant factor. Soft evidence takes the form of hunches and guess-work, is not amenable to scientific scrutiny, and is likened to the non-significant factor whose effect may exist but whose value is not established beyond reasonable doubt. The rule that one should use only significant factors corresponds to the making of decisions on the basis of hard evidence only. Clearly no organisation would survive if it held rigorously to such a view. Conversely, it would be unwise to rely *too* heavily on soft evidence and appropriate hard evidence should be used whenever possible. This converse view pertains equally in the context of empirical prediction studies.

Rarely will the data provide the only evidence available to the research worker and knowledge of the practical context and subjective assessments of the role of each variable should always be borne in mind. Often it is possible to use such knowledge in finding ways of combining together groups of related variables and replacing each group by one overall score defined in some appropriate way. Experience shows that the resultant loss of information in using such summary scores is more than offset by the greater precision with which a prediction equation based on a smaller number of factors can be fitted. When the data have been summarised as far as is possible in this way, it is probably best to fit a number of tentative prediction equations using various selections of the predictive factors and then (as discussed below) to base the final selection on an estimate of how accurately the corresponding prediction equation will predict the responses of future subjects.

The absurdity of expecting precise predictions of individual behaviour has already been stressed. Thus a prediction equation does not claim to forecast the behaviour of any given individual but rather the average behaviour of a group of like individuals. Although the outcome of tossing a coin is quite unpredictable, everyone will agree that to start a sports contest by the toss of a coin is 'fair'. This is because the chaos at the individual level is replaced by an order at the group level – the order being that, in a large group of tosses, heads will result almost exactly one-half of the time. The mechanics of a prediction equation is just an extension of this phenomenon. To see this, consider the particular response that is to be predicted: since the precise definition of this response will obviously vary from one study to another, let us denote it simply as y. Presumably, y, will be some aspect of dangerous offending. Similarly, we denote by $x_1, x_2, \ldots x_p$ the chosen predictive factors. Then a prediction equation assumes that y is some mathematical function of $x_1, x_2, \ldots x_p$ together with a further factor which might be called 'luck' or 'chance'. The presence of this chance effect for an individual's y corresponds to the 'chaos' referred to above; the 'order at the group level' corresponds to the fact that chance effects tend to cancel each other out when averaged over a large number of such individuals.

An example of a relatively simple prediction equation is taken from a recent study concerning a sample of patients in a maximum security hospital (Hinton, 1980). For each subject, data were compiled relating to social and medical history, and to the results of a number of psychometric and psychophysiological tests. As no follow-up information is available, aspects of a patient's past criminal record are taken as 'proxy' for the possible pattern of re-offending, on the basis that any factor or group of factors which indicate previous criminal behaviour might also be expected to be useful in prospective prediction. In this illustration, y is taken to be the 'variety of offences' defined as the number of types of offence on record, and three predictive factors are selected ($p = 3$). The corresponding prediction equation was fitted by the multiple regression computer routine in the SPSS package (Nie, Bent and Hull, 1970) giving the specification as follows:

$$\text{predicted variety} = 1\cdot27 - 0\cdot012 \times (V - P)$$
$$+ 0\cdot024 \times (\text{skin conductance}) \qquad (1)$$
$$+ 0\cdot057 \times (\text{drug frequency}),$$

$$\text{actual variety} = \text{predicted variety} + \text{random error}.$$

The three predictive factors are defined as:

$V - P$: Verbal intelligence score − Performance intelligence score, on the Wechsler Adult Intelligence Scale;

skin conductance: The time (in seconds) for an electrodermal response to recover halfway towards its original level following a signal; and

drug frequency: The (average) number of days per week on which the subject admitted taking drugs (excluding nicotine and alcohol).

The negative weight on $(V - P)$ supports the hypothesis that left temporal lobe deficit relates to 'psychotic' crime. The positive weights on the other two factors indicate that a slow recovery time in skin resistance, and a high level of drug dependence, are likewise associated with a high variety of offending.

Equation (1) takes the form of a series of additions or subtractions of the values of the predictive factors with weights determined by the statistical analysis. The assumption of additivity implied thereby is nearly always made in practice and is appropriate where y is measured on a continuous or an interval scale (or when, as in this case, the range of y is such as to make an interval scale reasonable). Obviously, terms are deleted or added to equation (1) if the value of p is less than or greater than 3 respectively.

In practice, however, the response y is often not of a continuous type, the case of a binary variable being perhaps the most common. Here y takes just two values according to the occurrence, or otherwise, of an event, such as re-offending within a stated interval of time. For instance, the study reported in Nuttall (1977) takes y to correspond to reconviction within two years after release from prison. Conventionally, a binary variable y is defined as 1 if the relevant event occurs and 0 otherwise, and so, superficially at least, can be taken as a numerically valued factor. Many authors, in fact, have fitted prediction equations of the type (1) even when y is a $0-1$ variable, and have interpreted the ensuing predicted value (equal to some decimal fraction) as the *probability* of the event in question. Although this works tolerably well when the predictive power of the data is low, it suffers from the obvious defect that equations such as (1) can take values which are negative or greater than 1, eventualities which are impossible for the value of a probability. Some instances of this approach are given in Mannheim and Wilkins (1955) and Simon (1971). A completely different approach, but one that is also defective on methodological grounds, is used in the study just referred to, Nuttall (1977).

What is probably the most powerful statistical method for fitting binary data is known as 'logistic regression'. This method works by transforming probabilities, which take values between 0 and 1, into 'logits', which can take any positive or negative numerical value. An equation similar to (1) is fitted to give the value of a predicted logit, which is then transformed back into a corresponding predicted probability. The method is used in the study discussed earlier in this chapter (Copas and Whiteley, 1976). The event in question is relapse (conviction or re-admission within two years), y is defined to be the probability of relapse, and the associated logit is predicted on the basis of six predictive factors covering items of social and criminal history. The exact form of this prediction equation is given in Table 1 of the cited paper. Although conceptually no more difficult than multiple regression equations such as (1), the fitting of logistic regression equations requires a rather more specialised computer programme such as that in Baker and Nelder (1978).

Table 10.1   *Fit of Prediction Equation in Copas and Whiteley (1976)*

Predicted probability (p)	Original cases		New cases	
	No.	%	No.	%
(i)	(ii)	(iii)	(iv)	(v)
0 to 0·3	14	21	12	33
0·3 to 0·5	33	36	21	43
0·5 to 0·7	19	63	29	52
0·7 to 1·0	38	87	25	72
	104	42	87	47

After the logistic regression prediction equation in Copas and Whiteley (1976) had been fitted on an initial sample of some hundred cases, it was checked on a further sample of new and independent cases who were likewise followed up for a period of two years after discharge. Table 10.1 of this chapter details the results of this validation check. Each sample of cases is divided into four groups according to the values of the predicted probabilities, p, as calculated from the prediction equation. The first group consists of cases with p less than 0·3 (the 'good' group), the second with p between 0·3 and 0·5 (the 'average/good' group), and similarly the 'average/poor' group with p between 0·5 and 0·7 and the 'poor' group with p over 0·7. In each group the actual percentage of cases who were observed to relapse is calculated as shown. The adequacy of the mathematical model is shown by the good agreement between these percentages for the initial cases (column (iii)) and the corresponding ranges in column (i). However, the agreement is much poorer when the percentages for the *new* cases (column (v)) are compared with these same ranges. For the 'good' group, the percentage of 33 per cent no longer lies in the range 0 to 0·3, and that for the 'poor' group (72 per cent) is only just in its range of 0·7 to 1. The two central groups have percentages much closer together than the corresponding figures in the initial series of cases. Since the overall rate of relapse in the original series is 42 per cent, it can be seen that the change in the percentages from column (iii) to column (v) is that of *regression towards the mean*. As judged by the performance on the new cases, the fitted probabilities tend to be too extreme – more accurate predictions would result if the predictions were adjusted inwards towards the overall average figure. This effect of condensing the predictions for the different cases towards the centre is sometimes termed 'shrinkage'. It has also been observed in many other prediction studies, and it can, in fact, be shown mathematically, that the tendency to 'shrink' is a necessary characteristic of any statistical fitting procedure.

Naturally, the amount of shrinkage will vary from one study to another. If a prediction equation is fitted from a very large number of cases the fitted constants in that equation will be quite accurately determined and so little shrinkage will result. For instance, the prediction equation in Nuttall (1977) is based on over 2,000 cases and the ensuing shrinkage appears to be minimal. Conversely, the smaller the sample size, and the more complicated the equation being fitted, the larger will be the shrinkage. The shrinkage can be particularly severe when the predictive factors used in the equation have been empirically selected from a much larger initial set of such factors.

The overall effect of shrinkage is that the accuracy with which a prediction equation predicts *future* cases is much more disappointing than might have been anticipated from the performance of that prediction equation in the context of the original data. This can also be seen in the shrinkage of the correlation coefficient between observed and predicted values. For example, the correlation coefficients between predicted probabilities and observed values of y in the study of Copas and Whiteley (1976) are 0.52 for the original series of cases, and 0.27 for the new series of cases; the correlation coefficient has shrunk to almost one-half of its original value. Similarly, substantial shrinkage has been observed in some of the studies reviewed in Simon (1971). All such studies have been characterised by a fairly complicated model fitted to a relatively small sample of cases. As remarked earlier, the effect is generally less marked for studies with more data and/or simpler models.

Using the mathematical theory developed in Copas (1980), it is possible (under certain technical assumptions) to anticipate in advance the shrinkage which is likely to be suffered by any particular prediction equation. The formula for the correlation coefficient is given in the appendix to this chapter in equation (A1). As an illustration, we return to the prediction equation (1) which was obtained in the maximum security hospital study mentioned earlier. The correlation coefficient between the predictions given by (1) and the observed values of y in the original data turned out to be 0.47 which, in the notation of the appendix, is taken to be the value of R. The three predictive factors used in (1) were in fact selected from a set of ten available factors, and the correlation coefficient between y and the predictions made by a prediction equation based on all ten factors was 0.56. The number of cases with complete information was 57. Thus, again in the notation of the appendix, we have $p = 3$, $p_0 = 10$, $n = 57$ and $R_0 = 0.56$. Inserting these values into (A1) gives a result of 0.25. Thus the correlation coefficient between predictions based on equation (1) and observed outcomes in *future* cases is estimated to 0.25 which, as in the studies cited above, represents a shrinkage of almost 50 per cent.

It is obvious that at the time a prediction equation is calculated in the context of any empirical study in dangerous offending (as in any other field), all available data will be used in the statistical analysis and no cases will be available for use in an independent check of the accuracy of that prediction equation. In practice, research workers have either proceeded with the publication of the details of their prediction equations and have tacitly ignored the likelihood of shrinkage, or else they have had to await the availability of data on a sufficiently large sample of new cases. Equation (A1) enables a forecast of the likely shrinkage to be made from information available from the initial sample only, and its calculation would form a simple appendage to the main statistical analysis. Although a full discussion of the mathematical reasoning behind equation (A1) would go outside the scope of this chapter, its calculation is well within the capabilities of a modest pocket calculator.

It has already been seen that when a prediction equation is tested on new cases the values of the predictions tend to be too extreme, and that greater accuracy would result if they were adjusted inwards towards the overall average figure. The amount of this adjustment is closely related to the degree of shrinkage in the correlation coefficient. Thus, if a prediction can be made of the correlation shrinkage, then an estimate can also be made of the required adjustment towards the mean. For prediction equations like (1), the adjustment is made by multiplying the whole prediction equation by a number K, which is less than 1, and then adding or subtracting a new constant term so as to leave the overall average value the same. The number K (which might be called the 'shrinkage factor') can be estimated from the original data by using the formula (A2) in the appendix. It can be proved that (under certain conditions) predictions made from an adjusted prediction equation will indeed be, on the average, unbiased estimates of the values of y for a sample of new and independent cases.

Using this technique, the value of K appropriate to (1) turns out to be 0·52, and so the adjusted prediction equation is

$$\text{predicted variety} = 1\cdot38 - 0\cdot0062 \times (V - P)$$
$$+ 0\cdot012 \times (\text{skin conductance}) \qquad (2)$$
$$+ 0\cdot030 \times (\text{drug frequency})$$

Each weight in (2) is simply the corresponding weight in (1) multiplied by 0·52. To demonstrate the effect of the adjustment introduced into this prediction equation, suppose a subject has values of the three predictive factors equal to − 15, 15 and 7 respectively. Then the predicted variety of offences from (1) is 2·21 and from (2) is 1·89. The overall average prediction from either equation is 1·49. Thus, this particular subject appears to be worse than average in the sense that the number of different types of offence is predicted to be greater, but the actual expected variety of offences for this subject is almost certainly smaller than is suggested by the figure of 2·21. Conversely, a subject whose prediction is below average is likely to have an actual expected variety of offences which is above that given by equation (1). The overall effect is to anticipate the quite severe shrinkage which characterises this particular study, and to end up with predictions for future cases which are substantially more modest than those that would (misleadingly) be given by a prediction equation fitted in the conventional way.

Full details of the mathematical arguments behind this method are given in Copas (1980). There is also a similarity with techniques proposed in two papers in the statistical literature, Stein (1960) and Stone (1974); see also the review in Draper and Van Nostrand (1979).

A very similar method of anticipating shrinkage is available when y is a dichotomous, or binary, variable. When the method of logistic regression is used, as in Copas and Whiteley (1976) and in Table 10.1, it is in the logit of the probability and not the probability itself which is predicted from a weighted sum of the predictive factors. This weighted sum is modified in exactly the same way as has been described in the context of equation (1) except that the necessary shrinkage factor K is given by equation (A3) instead of (A2). Once the modified value of the logit is obtained, it can be transformed back into the probability scale as before. The end result of the method is to move the predicted probabilities towards the overall average as has already been suggested from our examination of Table 10.1. The most noticeable change to this table is to increase the upper limit of the lowest category, and to decrease the lower limit of the highest category, thus bringing the ranges of predicted probability closer to the observed percentages given in the last column of that table (column (v)).

Although the correlation coefficient between the relevant criterion of dangerous offending and the various predictive factors is useful in assessing the information obtained in the data, it does not give an infallible guide to the actual accuracy of the predictions made by a prediction equation. To obtain a more direct measure of accuracy in the case of interval scale predictions, suppose that the prediction equation is applied to a new and independent case, after which the actual value of y is subsequently observed. Then the 'prediction error' is equal to

$$\text{actual } y - \text{predicted } y,$$

a quantity which will vary haphazardly from one new case to another. The average value of the square of such errors, or the 'prediction mean squared error', is perhaps the most appropriate measure of overall accuracy; a small value indicates a high degree of precision, a large value indicates a poor level of precision. An effective upper bound to the prediction mean squared error is given by considering the degenerate prediction equation which predicts y to be the overall average value regardless of the values of the predictive factors; the prediction mean squared error is then just the square of the standard deviation of y, say, s^2. Clearly, any prediction equation which leads to a prediction mean squared error in excess of s^2 is worse than useless, in the sense that better predictions could be obtained by ignoring the predictive factors altogether. The statistical value of a prediction equation can thus be judged by the proportional amount by which its prediction mean squared error falls below the value of s^2.

Making the same technical assumptions as in previous calculations, equation (A5) in the appendix shows how, given only the original data, an estimate of prediction mean squared error can be made. This formula allows for the not inconsiderable effect on shrinkage which arises from empirical selection of predictive factors, an effect which has nearly always been ignored in previous research. As an illustration, we again take the prediction equation given in (1). Inserting the appropriate values into (A5) gives a prediction mean squared error of 0.257. The value of s^2 here is 0.254, and so this is indeed an instance of the kind mentioned above. Thus equation (1), although fitted in the standard way and using the three most significant predictive factors, gives predictions which are no better, and even slightly worse, than one could obtain without the use of these predictive factors. In a sense, the original correlation of 0.47 between y and these three predictive factors (which has been quoted earlier) is a delusion – the severe shrinkage and uncertainty in the choice of these particular predictive factors renders the conventional methods ineffective. However, if the degree of shrinkage is estimated in advance, and the appropriate modifications made to the prediction equation as discussed above, then one can expect at least some modest improvement in the predictions. Equation (A4) in the appendix estimates the prediction mean squared error of a modified prediction equation which, as can be seen from the formulae, always gives a value which is smaller than (A5). For our illustration, equation (A4) gives the value 0.244, an improvement of some 4 per cent over the value of s^2. Clearly a modest improvement indeed, but one which faithfully reflects the rather low levels of correlation between the variety of offences and the predictive factors being considered. In other studies, with higher correlations and/or larger sample sizes, more useful levels of improvement are possible.

Perhaps it is hardly necessary to stress that prediction mean squared error, as for several of the other measures discussed earlier, is a *mean* in the proper sense of that word, namely, an average over a population of comparable circumstances. It has already been remarked that statistical methods operate at the level of the group rather than at the level of the individual. Thus the observed accuracy of a particular prediction equation for a particular sample of new cases will be influenced by a particular set of chance disturbances (or 'luck' in the terms of the earlier discussion), and so cannot be expected to correspond exactly to any specific forecasts such as those given by the formulae in the appendix. Such forecasts must be interpreted in the context of all possible data that might have been obtained. For example, suppose that a positive improvement in prediction mean squared error over the value of s^2 is anticipated. Then, if one were to imagine repeating the whole study again and again, the possibility of the accuracy of predictions being in fact worse cannot be ruled out, but the instances when this might occur would, in a sense, be outweighed by the majority of instances when the predictions would indeed be better than that implied by the value of s^2.

Summary and Conclusions

In this chapter we have discussed some questions which arise in the statistical analysis of data from studies of dangerous offending, with particular emphasis on just one aspect, the construction and validation of prediction equations. More fundamental questions of assessment and definition are, of course, taken up in other chapters of this book. Problems of study design have been only briefly mentioned but are no less important (see, for instance, Monahan, 1978). The tentative conclusions from this discussion might be listed as follows:

(1)   A preliminary statistical analysis of the data is nearly always worthwhile. Only simple descriptive methods are needed, mostly graphs and frequency tables. Besides the immediate aim of isolating factors which are likely to be useful as predictors, a preliminary analysis serves as a useful aid to understanding. Frequently, for example, some unexpected effect or association will be suggested by the data which leads to rethinking on the part of the research worker, and perhaps to redefinition and recoding of some of the items of information recorded in the study.

(2)   The performance of a prediction equation on new cases is generally worse than might have been anticipated from the original data. Given certain assumptions, the extent of this shrinkage can be predicted mathematically.

(3)   In some cases shrinkage can be so severe that conventional statistical methods (like regression analysis) are rendered virtually useless. Not infrequently have prediction equations been fitted in practice, apparently with useful results, only to find that when tested on future cases they appear to be almost totally void of the ability to predict. By anticipating the amount of shrinkage, however, a prediction equation can be modified using (A2) or (A3) so as to preserve at least some predictive power.

(4)   As an indication of the usefulness of a prediction equation, the correlation coefficient between observed and predicted values in the original data (which is nearly always quoted in practice) is too optimistic, and in some cases can be quite misleading. It is suggested that, when a prediction equation is fitted, a realistic assessment of its likeley performance on future cases should be made by using equations (A1), (A4) and (A5). If the value of (A4) is substantially lower than that of (A5), then the prediction equation should be modified by using (A2) or (A3). When a number of different prediction equations are fitted (as would normally be done in a complicated study), any choice between them should be made on the basis of such assessments and not simply on the basis of conventional measures of (retrospective) fit.

Mathematical Appendix

The following notation is used:

y = response being predicted
x_i = ith predictive factor
n = sample size
p = number of predictive factors selected
p_0 = total number of predictive factors available
R_0 = (multiple) correlation between y and all available x_i's
R = (multiple) correlation between y and the selected x_i's
$L = \dfrac{(n-1)R_0^2 - p_0}{R_0^2(n - p_0 - 1)}$
F = usual statistic for testing significance in the multiple regression of y on all available x_i's
χ^2 = usual statistic for testing significance in the analogous logistic regression
s = observed standard deviation of y
$D = ((n-1)R_0^2 - p_0)(R_0^2 - R^2) + p_0 R_0^2(1 - R_0^2).$

Shrinkage of Correlation

Under certain assumptions, the correlation between the predicted values given by a prediction equation and the actual values of y for *future* cases is estimated to be

$$RL \tag{A1}$$

Shrinkage Factors

The factor K is estimated by

$$K = 1 - \frac{p_0 - 2}{p_0 F} \tag{A2}$$

in the case of y being an interval scale measurement, and

$$K = 1 - \frac{p_0 - 2}{\chi^2} \tag{A3}$$

in the case of y being a binary response or dichotomy. The value of K is assumed to be between 0 and 1; if these formulae give values less than 0 or greater than 1 then K is truncated to 0 or 1 respectively.

Prediction Mean Squared Error

In the case of y being an interval scale measurement the prediction mean squared error of a modified prediction equation is estimated to be

$$\frac{(n-1)s^2}{n-p_0-1}\left(\frac{(n+1)(1-R_0^2)}{n}+\frac{LD}{(n-1)R_0^2}\right) \qquad (A4)$$

The corresponding prediction mean squared error of the unmodified prediction equation is estimated to be

$$(A4)+\left(\frac{Rsp_0(1-R_0^2)}{(n-p_0-1)R_0^2}\right)^2 \qquad (A5)$$

11 The Need for a Multidisciplinary Approach to the Study of 'Dangerousness'

JOHN W. HINTON

It is only fairly recently that the need for a co-operative broad-ranging multidisciplinary approach to the study of deviant behaviour has been recognised, though this is by no means universally accepted. What I hope to do in this chapter is to point out the limitations, as I see them, in criminological investigations which are restricted to one level of analysis. In this respect, I shall be following the views which Jeffery (1974) has propounded over the last ten years: that is, I shall attempt to show the limitations of purely physiological, mentalistic, or sociological approaches to the study of 'dangerousness' (using this term to mean the probability of wounding physical attacks on the person). I shall argue that biochemical and neurophysiological factors can provide the essential intervening variables – the missing links – in the environmental stimulus/response chain. It is proposed that environmental factors modify biological mechanisms which can then influence emotional, temperamental and some cognitive aspects of personality, which in turn can affect the type and magnitude of aggressive acts and the capacity for social conditioning and empathy.

I shall first attempt to give some indications of the present situation in regard to the diagnosis, treatment and release of offenders in maximum security hospitals. I will try to show how, in various ways, maintenance of the status quo is inimical both to psychobiological research and to the subsequent development of statistical prediction methods based on a wide spectrum of objective sociobiological data.

Putting it very crudely, maximum security patients can be divided into the 'mad' and the 'bad'. Those labelled 'psychopaths' are thought to be 'bad'. To have 'psychopathy' is considered socially a 'bad thing'. In most people's minds the term 'psychopath' is synonymous with 'dangerousness' and 'violence' – both emotive and generally ill-defined concepts. The problem of classifying psychopathy is emphasised by Treves Brown (1977) in a critical review article entitled 'Who is the psychopath?'. He extensively documents the varying, often discrepant, attempts of many practising psychiatrists to define the 'psychopath'. He points out the paradox in the approach of professional workers; I quote: 'Although psychopathy is often considered by definition to be untreatable, professional staff often continue to treat psychopaths.' (Indeed, 30 to 40 per cent of the intake of a large maximum security hospital in the UK is of individuals labelled 'psychopathic deviate'. The fact that they are called 'patients' surely assumes that some form of medical treatment is required.) Treves Brown concludes: 'either those with experience of the condition do not regard it as untreatable, or the professional staff are displaying psycho-pathic characteristics themselves by giving treatment knowing it to be ineffective'. In practice, we have a situation where custodial detention itself may sometimes euphemistically be referred to as 'clinical treatment'. However, if he becomes violent, the diagnosed psychopath may be deemed in need of a major tranquilliser. Because he seems unmanageable, the patient may be judged to be lacking responsibility, and therefore the doctor can feel justified in a forced prescription which has the advantage of making the patient manageable.

Following on from Treves Brown's analysis, it is interesting to note that ex-security hospital patients, frequently classed as psychopaths, who grossly re-offend in exactly the same way as before, are sent to prison. Why is this? Why, on the second occasion of conviction, should they be judged *not* to be in need of special hospitalisation? Are they less 'ill' the second time round? Or were the doctors wrong in the first place? Perhaps they were judged to have been successfully 'treated' the first time and may be they are judged to be untreatable on the subsequent conviction, though perhaps more 'dangerous'.

Responsible medical officers in security hospitals may try to argue that decisions to release and admit are made on medical criteria, but such decisions are not arrived at without reference to the type of crime, the social context and potential political repercussions. Furthermore, while indiscriminate factors are involved in determining referrals (as described by Treves Brown in Chapter 4), in the case of re-offending, 'public opinion' can be a major influence. Considering the operation of the system at present, there seems to be a case for assessing 'dangerousness' without reference to any so-called 'mental condition'.

So much for the 'bad'. Let us now consider the 'mad'. Currently, aggres-sive or sexual offenders are considered as particularly dangerous if they are designated 'insane'. Today the term 'schizophrenic' has displaced that of 'lunatic' and we now have the 'lunatic' (thought-disordered person) classed under various so-called 'psychotic' conditions. Wing's WHO study (1971) is well known for pointing out the idiosyncratic nature of diagnoses of schizophrenia. Furthermore, there appear to be many kinds of schizophrenia. Out of fifty or more maximum security hospital patients who were labelled 'schizophrenic' and whom we tested under highly standardised conditions, we saw no two so-called 'schizophrenics' displaying similar abnormal behavioural characteristics, let alone schizophrenic symptomatology. However, in a security hospital, the general label of 'schizophrenia' can have general implications for treat-ment and discharge. As a brief digression, it may be of interest to compare the above observations with the experience of my recent research team, while studying a sample of 170 male offenders in a Scottish short-stay prison. This prison mainly deals with recidivistic petty offenders, yet we found that approximately 5 per cent of these showed obvious types of thought disorder, making them impossible to interview. Since they are in prison, these people were presumably regarded as sane by the courts. If one of this 5 per cent happened to have committed a murder, I believe that judged 'mental state' could then lead to maximum security hospitalisation. The magnitude of the crime could force 'mental state' to be taken into account, and a medical label or diagnosis would be used to legitimise indeterminate detention.

Psychologists and other social scientists are well aware of the circularity of psychiatric diagnoses, yet the more that specialised jargon increases in this field, the more respectable may the expert's opinion be seen to be. This is a dangerous development. I believe that because of its unscientific nature and its gross implications for the individual's freedom, this process of labelling is immoral. An individual's fate can be affected by the label he is given by a doctor, and as Wilkins (1962) has indicated this is a 'faith in intangibles'. Each psychiatrist may be seen as an idiosyncratically and inadequately programmed computer – to quote Wilkins: 'a clinician has only his own sample to guide him, with no guarantee of its lack of bias'. In coming to independent objective conclusions when defining people on behavioural criteria of 'dangerousness', it is essential to have some objective measurable factors and standardised scientific procedures. I suggest that in the present position of ignorance, diagnostic labelling should be discontinued. This would be the honest course of action in most cases. The implications of stopping diagnostic labelling would probably be a reduction in the power of the psychiatrist generally and an increase in the likelihood of the adoption of a more flexible behavioural approach to assessment and treatment of offenders with, hopefully, less reliance on drugs. Doctors should, I think, pronounce on potential dangerousness *only* when brain damage or neuro-endocrinological abnormalities can be *unequivocally* demonstrated, and where these are *known* to increase very significantly the likelihood of gross antisocial violent behaviour. In our present state of knowledge such pronouncements would be very infrequent.

We must, however, guard against spurious scientific objectivity, and in this regard one important question we should consider is the effect on the detainee of discovering measurable abnormalities such as some EEG or chromosome abnormality. How does this information currently affect psychiatrists' recommendations for discharge? If a male inmate has an extra Y chromosome, does this affect decision-making? What is the effect of finding EEG theta predominancy? Does this affect decision-making? The fact is, there are more people living civilised lives in the community with XYY and 'excess' theta than there are in security establishments. It is only true that the prison and security hospital populations contain a small but higher proportion of people with these abnormalities – but no one knows the psychological or social significance of these deviations. That is not to deny that it may ultimately prove useful to include these factors with a small loading in a prediction equation, but in the present state of knowledge these abnormalities should, I contend, be ignored in decision-making on dangerousness. The research work has yet to be conducted which will decide the right domain of variables and which will determine the weighting to be placed on these variables. When this has been done, it might be possible to satisfy the objective requirements which ethical decision-making demands.

How does the psychologist currently fit into the maximum security hospital scene? My past research team fortunately operated in a scientific capacity on the periphery, but clinical psychologists actually working within the system are, I believe, in a dilemma. Clinical psychologists are ancillary to psychiatrists. The medical officer is responsible for decision-making on admission, discharge and treatment. He may be seen by the patient as judge, jury and jailor. I submit that clinical psychologists should ask themselves to what extent their professional status is being jeopardised in so far as they might inadvertently pander to the requirement of the medical profession for assessments which are used to 'back-up' psychiatric labels. By this I mean carrying out assessments on referrals, particularly using instruments developed to satisfy psychiatric requirements, such as the MMPI and certain psychiatric Nurses' Rating Scales. It may be said that any psychologist who provides such assistance to 'keep the psychiatrist happy' (and it does happen) is engaging in a practice which is unjustifiable on scientific grounds and therefore unethical – particularly so in the security setting of indeterminate detention. There are no adequate psychological tests for assessing aspects of dangerous behaviour, yet psychologists are expected to provide assessments on security patients, frequently using tests which have been developed on other populations. The question of professional ethics arises here for the psychologist. Restrictions (such as the Official Secrets Act in the UK) and the power of the medical profession in security hospitals ensure that those who are prepared to work in these authoritarian settings cannot speak openly about the situation, and therefore, by continuing to work in such institutions, individuals may be seen, by outsiders, to be acquiescing in the system. If a professional employee (for example, a psychologist or social worker) openly questions a method of assessment or treatment (without full prior medical approval) he could be labelled a 'security risk'. How can this situation provide a satisfactory basis for open scientific research and interdisciplinary co-operation, on the problems of dangerousness, within security hospitals? I would like to suggest that a strong case could be made for regular consultation with outside bodies, especially recognised Civil Liberty groups, in planning assessment, treatment and research.

Government reports recommending interdisciplinary co-operation in decision-making in maximum security hospitals, for example the Aarvold Report (1973), are of little use in changing the system, as long as one section of one profession – namely, psychiatrists – are in the ultimate position of responsibility for making recommendations on 'dangerousness', with clinical psychologists being seen by them either as a potential professional threat, or a medical appendage. However, it has to be admitted that to date, there are no validated research results to give the psychologist confidence in providing advice on the discharge of offenders.

It seems reasonable to suggest that the collection of evidence and conduct of research on the behaviour of those labelled 'dangerous' should be controlled by behavioural scientists – namely, professional psychologists, working with other disciplines. A case can be made for inclusion of sociologists for study of socio-economic and other past and future environmental factors which could relate to 'dangerousness'. In predicting probability of violent behaviours, the weighting of data would require defined statistical procedures, but until the research has been done to decide precisely what variables are of relevance, it is difficult to justify indeterminate sentences, largely imposed by psychiatric 'experts' who also have the power of release.

While it is clear that present assessment procedures will continue in security hospitals, some clinical psychologists have emphasised that there should be a continual research drive for the incorporation of more objective methods and psychological data. Because of the breadth of his discipline (from biology to sociology) and his training in research methods, it may be thought that the psychologist is theoretically and practically in a central position for integrating research of a multidisciplinary nature in this field. However, in the present situation the institutional psychologist is not able to initiate or control such research effectively. The problems involved will be discussed more fully later in the chapter.

While there are problems in the mentalistic approach of psychometrics, one alternative direction for the psychologist is in the development and application of neuropsychological tests. The work of Flor-Henry (1976) and Lorne Yeudall (1977) in Canada is an example of this in criminology. Using the revised Halstead-Reitan battery, Lorne Yeudall claims to have demonstrated a considerable relationship between psychopathic criminal behaviour and functional abnormalities associated with localised brain damage, and the Canadian Federal Penitentiary Service has engaged him to conduct investigations in this area. He suggests that the multivariate approach, which he intends to use, calls for a new discipline of 'neuro-sociology' involving the systematic integration of neurological, psychological and sociological information. However, the claims currently made by Yeudall regarding the relationship between psychopathy and functional brain damage are to be treated with caution. There are problems with the definition of psychopathy and the inferences from multivariate methods employed. (Hinton, 1981.)

The research of Hare (1968, 1978), Schalling (1978) and Mednick (1975) has related psychophysiological functioning to antisocial behaviour and criminal recidivism. The studies of Mednick (1975) and Venables (1977) also suggest a genetic predisposition to thought disorder and criminality. These researchers have reported specific electrodermal characteristics relating to antisocial behaviour – findings which have also been demonstrated by Hinton and Woodman (1977) and which have subsequently been confirmed in an extended study with larger samples of security patients (Hinton, O'Neill and Dishman, 1979).

The clinical or prison psychologist is theoretically in a key position to enlist the co-operation of custodians or nurses in obtaining objective ratings of behaviour over extended periods of time. In practice, this involves a considerable amount of time, effort, persuasion and management skill. Whether this effort is worthwhile is open to doubt given the analysis presented by me in Chapter 7. In our research we developed rating scales for security hospitals (Hinton, 1975; Hinton, O'Neill and Dishman, 1979) and confirmed that behaviour rating by nurses on 'trouble-stirring' behaviour (in well-institutionalised patients) related to reported psychophysiological indications of antisocial recidivism, while ratings on 'communication and perceptual abnormalities' correlated well with electrodermal measures which have been found to relate to thought disorder (Venables, 1977) and primary psychopathic behaviour (Schalling, 1978; Mednick, 1975). However, behaviour in an institution may not relate to behaviour outside it.

It would seem that psychologists are optimally placed for conducting and co-ordinating research on the psychopharmacological effects of drugs, by virtue of their expertise in methods of assessment of treatment response, namely, conducting behaviour ratings, psychophysiological assessment and neuropsychological tests. With current developments in biochemistry, in the discovery of hormones which control brain functions relating to drives and emotions, and with the advent of a new technology in this field which allows for the rapid and accurate measurement of hormones existing in small quantities in body fluids, a case can be made for the incorporation of extensive biochemical data in criminological research, including psychopharmacological studies on the modificaiton of different types of aggressive behaviour, *given fully informed consent*. However, there are problems of assessment and standardisation of the behaviour of the custodians and the ward regimen. Collaboration with the medical profession for the prescription of drugs and the removal of some body-fluids may also present problems.

It could be argued that there are also external factors which hinder psychopharmacological research on the behaviour modification effects of drugs on patients in maximum security institutions. Research appears to be thwarted quite frequently by the response of groups whose arguments for human rights, while admirable, are sometimes perhaps shortsighted, bearing in mind both the interests of gross offenders as a whole in the long term and the dearth of knowledge about the effects of drug therapies currently prescribed in large doses for behaviour disorders. As Cole (1977) pointed out, the response on the part of US prison administrators has been to stop *all* research rather than be 'hassled' by angry groups in the community.

Another problem, particularly in regard to maximum security hospitals and the security wings of mental hospitals, is that we have reached the situation where the use of 'knockout' tranquillisers may be considered desirable to reduce violence to staff (by making detainees compliant) –although a doctor may convince himself that this is in the best interests of the patient whom he might judge to be not responsible for his behaviour. Researchers asking for changes of drug regimes could therefore be seen as a threat to the security of custodians – putting them at risk. Thus there is resistance to the carrying out of research which could precipitate an industrial dispute. Quite simply, I am suggesting that the extensive use of major tranquillisers can inhibit essential research on habitually aggressive individuals. At the same time, the use of massive doses of phenothyazines over long periods of time can not only produce a compliant 'zombie', but also may cause permanent damage to brain function.

Several behaviour modifying drugs, which have been released over the past five years, are very relevant for research on the modification of antisocial behaviour and thought disordered schizophrenia. These drugs are ethical in so far as they have no observable side-effects, but there is no prospect of conducting psychopharmacological research. The problem remains that medical authorities in custodial institutions are in general fairly inflexible and have no wish to risk instigating staff problems. Well-established hospitals have become 'closed institutions', with the staff generally resistant to change. The result of this is that almost any research is made difficult. The situation is exacerbated by researchers, largely psychologists, who are seen by the established staff as merely using the institution and contributing nothing. In my experience, this phenomenon of the 'fleeting researcher' is general in prisons, borstals and security hospitals, and it can naturally provoke staff resentment and lack of co-operation. One answer to the problem would be the very long-term funding of criminological research programmes, which entails the active involvement of, and communication with, institution staff at all levels, as well as extensive communication with patients. If this can be achieved, it might be possible to conduct psychological research on behaviour-normalising drugs, but at present this seems inconceivable.

It is, I believe, important to view the use of drugs not from the management standpoint, but from the point of view of *normalising* the biochemical and neurophysiological functioning of patients so that behaviour modification techniques can be made effective, and the development of 'self-control' made possible. All such treatments should be on an informed voluntary basis in every case. It may then be possible to release more inmates on medication and/or under clinical supervision. In our present state of knowledge, however, it may well be in the interests of patients or inmates in Special Hospitals to return to simple physical methods of restraint, if and when absolutely necessary. The alternative is to continue to use large doses of tranquillising drugs for long periods of time in order to keep patients passive. As already mentioned, many such drugs currently in use can produce adverse side-effects and permanent neurological and endocrinological damage. Superficially, the rejection of drugs may seem a step back, but as I have argued, it could set the stage for a leap forward in the treatment of offenders labelled 'dangerous' by providing a situation which allows valid urgently needed research. I must however stress my concern for careful supervision to ensure ethical procedures, and I would recommend that researchers in this field should consult with, and actively involve, respected civil libertarian organisations.

So far I have ignored the general approach of criminologists, namely, sociological and environmental study. It is, I believe, very important for any multidisciplinary research team to include research sociologists in dealing with case record data such as educational and work record, drug and drink problems, institutionalisation, home background, the variety and types of conviction and the relationship of the offender to the victim.

Unfortunately, among criminologists there has been an unwillingness to view biological variables as critical to criminal behaviour, as Jeffery (1974) points out in his paper on genetics and criminology. Jeffery refers to American criminologists, but I think his point applies in the UK as well.

Criminologists tend to look to the social environment for causation and follow Durkheim's anti-reductionism thesis as a dogma. But as indicated by Jeffery, in the light of recent developments in genetics and biology, it is no longer reasonable to take the view that there is an antithesis between biological and environmental factors (in fact there is continuous inter-action). He argues against 'mentalistic determinism' – the reliance on questionnaires and interviews to infer 'mental state' and hence propensity for criminal behaviour – though there may be some case for psychometrics as indicated by Blackburn in this volume. Jeffery advocates direct behavioural observation, but also points out the inadequacy of the simple-minded 'environmental determinism' of the strict Skinnerian behaviour-ist. The 'physical determinism' model which Jeffery proposes puts neurophysiological and biochemical factors as essential intervening variables which, I believe, is quite reasonable (Hinton, 1981). He proposes that we should replace the term 'mental illness' with 'behavioural disorders'. Thus concepts like 'mental state' and the 'mind' are thrown out. (It is interesting to note that Tennant, a doctor with criminological train-ing, and previous director of the UK Special Hospitals Research Unit, in a 1971 article on the dangerous offender dismissed biological factors as of no particular significance. His approach was mentalistic and environmentally deterministic, combining psychiatric and sociological outlooks in assess-ing 'dangerousness'. In general, attitudes of forensic psychiatrists have changed little since then, despite the considerable advances in psychology and biology which Jeffery points out.)

Aggressive and emotional reactions are partly the product of previous general modifications of neurological and/or endocrinological functioning in phylogenetically primitive structures in mammals. The effect of early handling experiences in promoting hormone response abnormalities, which relate to fearfulness, have been demonstrated by the animal research of Levine (1969) and others, while Bagshaw and Kimble (1972) have demonstrated that there are relationships in monkeys between the function of the limbic system, psychophysiological responses and abnormal behaviour. On the basis of the latter research, Venables (1977) has pro-posed a neurological link between aspects of limbic function, thought disorder and psychophysiological functioning. 'Brain and behaviour' research on animals can also be related to aggressive antisocial behaviour in humans, when considering certain aspects of limbic function. Thus it is important for criminologists and sociologists to take biological factors into account, just as biochemists and neurologists must not ignore environ-mental factors which influence hormone levels and neural functions.

Following on from the research on pain and pleasure centres of the brain, Jeffery (1974) proposes that 'if we regard pleasure and pain as basic components of human behaviour and its motivation, we can then state that criminal behaviour is learned behaviour that is mediated by the limbic system of the brain'. For the future of criminology, Jeffery advocates a multidisciplinary team to deal with factors in the organism and in the environment. He considers that we should combine a number of disci-plines for co-operative team research in criminology, and I would agree with this (Table 11.1).

Table 11.1 *Interdisciplinary Research in Criminology: a Modification of the List of Jeffery (1974)*

Organism	Environment
Behavioural genetics	Learning theory
Neurophysiology	Environmental psychology
Psychopharmacology	Criminology
Psychometrics	Sociology
Neuropsychology	Urban planning
Neuroendocrinology	Economics
Psychophysiology	Criminal law
Physiological psychology	Penology
	Victimology
	Social psychology

Jeffery claims that this multidisciplinary team should focus on the prevention of crime rather than punishment or treatment. However, psychopharmacological research essentially studies the effects of treatment and this is arguably an important and legitimate area of study, particularly in the testing of hypotheses generated by psychophysiological and behavioural studies. Without experimental studies, many correlational studies remain inconclusive. Ethical problems arise particularly in the area of treatment, but given sufficient vetting of studies and the safeguard of fully informed consent, these are not insurmountable.

On the question of what case record data to study, it is worthwhile considering the outcome of prospective research such as that of Farrington (1976) and the Broadmoor patient follow-up of Black (1977). There are prediction problems with purely case record criteria. As emphasised time and again at the NATO Conference on Computer Prediction in Parole, convened by Dieter Girmes at Cambridge University in 1976, there is considerable shrinkage on replication from the construction sample results to the validation sample results. This is well illustrated by Farrington's work, where combinations of variables proved to be little better than the best single case record predictor of juvenile official delinquency. Such problems are emphasised by Professor Copas in this book. Thus one major difficulty in using only sociological data is the considerable interdependence of the environmental variables. 'Biological factors' could here provide the extra dimensions. I propose that shrinkage would be reduced considerably if combinations of variables from many dissimilar levels of analysis were included. Reliance on case record data or personality assessment is a major limitation. In any case, personality test data suffer from massive faking problems in institutions and especially under indeterminate detention. It must be recognised, however, that environmental factors – including chance factors (like meeting the right marriage partner) – after release from institutions have to be taken into account in follow-up studies. I think that where possible in post-discharge research, assessment of future socio-economic and other difficulties should be conducted at the time of release, and such data included in any prediction equation.

A major difficulty with the research that my group carried out in a security hospital is that it was inevitably retrospective (Hinton, 1980; Woodman and Hinton, 1978b). All we could do was to observe how our psychophysiological variables related to case record and other behavioural criteria which, on theory and available evidence, we expected to be relevant to various defined aspects of 'dangerousness'. I have more recently been involved in a prospective multidisciplinary follow-up study of prisoners. Psychophysiological indices, relevant hormone measures and case background data have been obtained, together with assessments of future problems. The progress of released prisoners is being followed over the following three years to test out predictions on future propensity for violence and recidivism, on the basis of prediction equations developed by Professor John Copas (1980), who carried out the Henderson prediction study with Stuart Whiteley (1976). For future research, therefore, I continue to take the view of Leslie Wilkins (1962) who in the early 1960s eloquently argued that there is no place for unmeasurable clinical intuition in criminological endeavour. If data can be simply categorised or presented on an interval scale, it can be considered suitable for the development of a prediction equation – though, as Professor Copas points out here, non-linear methods are necessary.

In looking at the need for long-term research and the development of prediction equations, we have to be realistic, and at the present time there seems little prospect of long-term research funding. There is a strong case for prospective criminological research starting before the nursery stage and extending over twenty years, but for financial and ethical/political reasons this seems quite out of the question. To be realistic, I think one is forced to pessimism.

For convicted individuals considered potentially dangerous, perhaps we should aim for statistical assessment procedures where several multi-variate equations are devised, based on a limited number of key weighted variables, and covering a wide span of disciplines. For example, the equations might give (*a*) the probability of indiscriminate re-offending and (*b*) the probability of a crime of murderous intensity. This takes into account two of the aspects of dangerousness which Walker mentioned in his chapter, and the aspect of 'vivid danger' analysed here by Bottoms and Brownsword.

I have constructed a speculative diagrammatic illustration of these two dimensions in Figure 11.1. This figure shows a *possible* relationship between antisocial behaviour and some psychophysiological measures of anxiety reactions and emotional reactivity. It summarises some of the main published results to date from a five-year maximum security hospital study. Roughly, the vertical dimension represents past propensity for murderous personal attack, which has biochemical correlates, while the horizontal dimension represents probability of past indiscriminate offending, which has electrodermal correlates. Thus, the greatest 'public risk' would be presented by the individuals falling in the top right-hand quadrant – with high noradrenaline to adrenaline ratio and low electrodermal spontaneous activity plus slow orienting response recovery. This approach may be seen as providing an index of propensities which environmental stressors and conditioning could potentiate and precipitate. The social, economic and other stress factors *must* be assessed and included in any prediction of future behaviour. Nothing more is claimed of the model at the present time than that it illustrates one aspect of the type of multidisciplinary approach I am advocating and that it is amenable to objective tests.

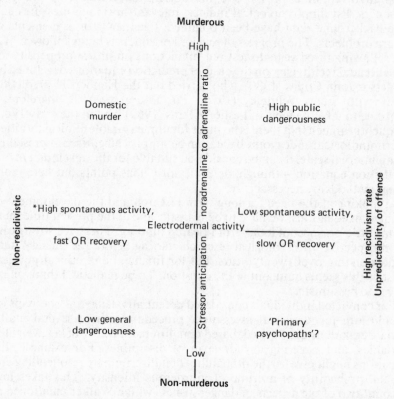

* Spontaneous electrodermal activity correlates with test anxiety (Hinton *et al.*, 1979).

Figure 11.1   *Speculative dimensional schema of dangerousness showing some possible biochemical and psychophysiological correlates (based on retrospective data).*

In conclusion and as an eventual ideal (given the continuation of indeterminate detention) multidisciplinary prediction equations could eventually be introduced as part of a parole assessment procedure for 'dangerous' offenders. Such procedures would need to be subject to regular and frequent review, and modified as necessary in the light of new data as it came to hand. A continuing post-discharge follow-up study would be considered an essential prerequisite to the institution of this type of parole assessment. Judgements concerning indeterminate detention, based on the clinical experience of psychiatrists, could be replaced by rulings presented by non-medical administrators and determined by probability measures. It is suggested that the level of 'fail safe' should not be a medical decision but could be a legal one. In my opinion, responsibility for decision-making in regard to potential recidivism and violent attack should be vested in the legal profession, working with the advice of statisticians, probably operating with biosocial data and perhaps along the lines developed and described by Professor Copas in Chapter 10. However, in the light of present knowledge, and for ethical reasons, I would support the finite sentence for the vast majority of those currently considered dangerous (as Bottoms and Brownsword argue in Chapter 2). Such finite sentences may have the immediate advantages of forcing the introduction of more therapeutic treatment for detainees, improving post-discharge care of currently so-called 'dangerous' offenders and promoting much-needed research.

As an addendum, I must emphasise that the somewhat polemical views expressed in this chapter are entirely my own and should not be linked to any government department or institution. Because of the operation of the British Official Secrets Act, I am in no position to state my sources of information or provide substantiation of many of the opinions I have expressed.

Acknowledgements

This chapter was completed while the author was in receipt of grants from the Scottish Home and Health Department, the Social Science Research Council and the Manpower Services Commission. Thanks are due to the Departments of Forensic Medicine and Psychology at the University of Glasgow for facilities provided.

References

Aarvold, D., Hill, D. and Newton, G. P. (1973), *Report on the Review of Procedures for the Discharge and Supervision of Psychiatric Patients Subject to Special Restrictions*, Cmnd 5191 (London: HMSO).

Abel, G. G., Barlow, D. H. and Blanchard, E. B. (1973), 'Developing heterosexual arousal by altering masturbatory fantasies: a controlled study', paper presented to the Association for Advancement of Behavior Therapy, Miami, December.

Abel, G. G. and Blanchard, E. B. (1976), 'The measurement and generation of sexual arousal in male sexual deviates', in *Progress in Behaviour Modification*, Vol. 2, ed. M. Hersen, R. M. Eisler and P. M. Miller (London: Academic Press).

Abel, G. G., Blanchard, E. B., Barlow, D. H. and Mavissakalian, M. (1975), 'Identifying specific erotic cues in sexual deviations by audio-taped descriptions', *Journal of Applied Behavior Analysis*, vol. 8, pp. 58–71.

Abel, G. G., Blanchard, E. B. and Becker, J. V. (1976), 'Psychological treatment of rapists', in *Sexual Assault*, ed. M. J. Walker and S. L. Brodsky (Lexington, Mass.: D. C. Heath (Lexington Books)).

Adams-Webber, J. R. (1979), *Personal Construct Theory* (Chichester: Wiley).

Advisory Council on the Penal System (1978), *Sentences of Imprisonment* (London: HMSO).

Alston, W. (1975), 'Traits, consistency, and conceptual alternatives for personality theory', *Journal of the Theory of Social Behaviour*, vol. 5, pp. 17–45.

Amir, M. (1971), *Patterns in Forcible Rape* (Chicago: University of Chicago Press).

Appleyard, W. J. (1970), 'Social factors influencing hospital admission of children', *Developmental Medicine and Child Neurology*, vol. 12, pp. 226–7.

Arnold, L. S. and Quinsey, V. L. (1977), 'Overcontrolled hostility among men found not guilty by reason of insanity', *Canadian Journal of Behavioural Science*, vol. 9, no. 4, pp. 330–40.

Athens, L. H. (1980), *Violent Criminal Acts and Actors: A Symbolic Interactional Study* (London: Routledge & Kegan Paul).

Ax, A. (1953), 'The physiological differentiation between fear and anger in humans', *Psychosomatic Medicine*, vol. 14, pp. 433–42.

Axelrod, J., Mueller, R. A., Henry, J. P. and Stephens, P. M. (1970), 'Changes in enzymes involved in the biosynthesis and metabolism of noradrenaline and adrenaline after psychosocial stimulation', *Nature*, vol. 225, pp. 1059–60.

Bagshaw, M. H. and Kimble, D. P. (1972), 'Bimodal EDR orienting response characteristics in limbic lesioned monkeys: correlates with schizophrenic patients', paper presented to the Society for Psychophysiological Research, Boston.

Baker, R. J. and Nelder, J. A. (1978), *Generalized Linear Interactive Models* (Oxford: Numerical Algorithms Group).

Bancroft, J. (1970), 'A comparative study of aversion and desensitization in the treatment of homosexuality', in *Behaviour Therapy in the Seventies*, ed. L. E. Burns and J. L. Worsley (Bristol: Wright).

Bancroft, J. (1971), 'The application of psychophysiological measures to the assessment and modification of sexual behaviour', *Behaviour Research and Therapy*, vol. 9, pp. 119–30.

Bancroft, J. (1974), *Deviant Sexual Behaviour: Modification and Assessment* (Oxford: Clarendon Press).

Bancroft, J. (1977), 'Mongol sexuality', *The Practitioner* (Notes and Queries), vol. 218, p. 341.

Bannister, D. and Mair, J. M. M. (1968), *The Evaluation of Personal Constructs* (London: Academic Press).

Barbaree, H. E., Marshall, W. L. and Lanthier, R. D. (1979), 'Deviant sexual arousal in rapists', *Behaviour Research and Therapy*, vol. 17, pp. 215–72.

Barlow, D. H. (1973), 'Increasing heterosexual responsiveness in the treatment of sexual deviation: a review of the clinical and experimental evidence', *Behaviour Therapy*, vol. 4, pp. 655–71.

Barlow, D. H. (1976), 'Assessment of sexual behaviour', in *Handbook of Behavioural Assessment*, ed. K. S. Calhoun and H. E. Adams (New York: Wiley).

Barlow, D. H., Abel, G. G., Blanchard, E. B., Bristow, A. R. and Young, L. D. (1977), 'A heterosexual skills behavior checklist for males', *Behaviour Therapy*, vol. 8, pp. 229–39.

Barlow, D. H. and Agras, W. S. (1973), 'Fading to increase heterosexual responsiveness in homosexuals', *Journal of Applied Behavior Analysis*, vol. 6, pp. 355–66.

Barlow, D. H., Agras, W. S., Abel, G. G., Blanchard, E. B. and Young, L. D. (1975), 'Biofeedback and reinforcement to increase heterosexual arousal in homosexuals', *Behaviour Research and Therapy*, vol. 3, pp. 45–50.

Barlow, D. H., Leitenberg, H. and Agras, W. S. (1969), 'The experimental control of sexual deviation through manipulation of the noxious scene in covert sensitization', *Journal of Abnormal Psychology*, vol. 74, pp. 596–601.

Bayley, N. and Shaefer, E. S. (1960), 'Relationship between socioeconomic variables and behaviour of mothers toward young children', *Journal of General Psychology*, vol. 96, pp. 61–8.

Beck, A. T. (1979), *Cognitive Therapy of Depression* (New York: Guilford).

Becker, W. C. (1960), 'The matching of behaviour rating and questionnaire personality factors', *Psychology Bulletin*, vol. 57, pp. 201–12.

Becker, W. C. (1964), *Review of Child Development Research*, Vol. 1 (New York: Russell Sage Foundation).

Berkowitz, L. (1969), 'The frustration-aggression hypothesis revisited', in *Roots of Aggression*, ed. L. Berkowitz (New York: Atherton).

Berkowitz, L. (1977), 'Situational and personal conditions governing reactions to aggressive cues', in *Personality at the Crossroads*, ed. D. Magnusson and N. S. Endler (Hillsdale: Erlbaum).

Bieber, B., Bieber, I., Dain, H., Dince, P., Drelick, M., Grundlack, R., Kromer, M., Wilber, C. and Bieber, T. (1963), *Homosexuality* (New York: Basic Books).

Black, D. A. (1963), 'Psychometrics of defensiveness', paper presented at the Quarterly Meeting of the Royal Medical Association, Broadmoor, May.

Black, D. A. (1977), 'A five-year follow-up study of male patients discharged from Broadmoor Hospital', paper presented at the Annual Conference of the British Psychological Society, Exeter.

Blackburn, R. (1968), 'Personality in relation to extreme aggression in psychiatric offenders', *British Journal of Psychiatry*, vol. 114, no. 7, pp. 821–8.

Blackburn, R. (1971), 'Personality types among abnormal homicides', *British Journal of Criminology*, vol. 11, no. 1, pp. 14–31.

Blackburn, R. (1972), 'Dimensions of hostility and aggression in abnormal offenders', *Journal of Consulting and Clinical Psychology*, vol. 38, pp. 20–6.

Blackburn, R. (1973), 'A study of impulsivity in abnormal offenders', doctoral dissertation, University of Southampton.

Blackburn, R. (1974), *Development and Validation of Scales to Measure Hostility and Aggression*, Special Hospitals Research Report no. 12 (London: Special Hospitals Research Unit).

Blackburn, R. (1975), 'An empirical classification of psychopathic personality', *British Journal of Psychiatry*, vol. 127, pp. 456–60.

Blackburn, R (1979), 'Psychopathy and personality: the dimensionality of self-report and behaviour rating data in abnormal offenders', *British Journal of Social and Clinical Psychology*, vol. 18, pp. 111–19.

Blackburn, R. (1980), 'Personality and the criminal psychopath: a logical analysis and some empirical data', in *Lo Psicopatico Delinquente*, Facolta di Giurisprudenza, Universitata di Messina (Milan: Giuffre).

Boozer, G. (1975), 'Offender treatment: programming (workshop)', paper presented at the Sixth Alabama Symposium on Justice and the Behavioral Sciences, University of Alabama, Tuscaloosa, Alabama, January.

Bottoms, A. E. (1977), 'Reflections on the renaissance of dangerousness', *Howard Journal of Penology and Crime Prevention*, vol. 16, pp. 70–96.

Bottoms, A. E. (1981), 'Selected issues in the dangerousness debate', in *The Assessment of Dangerousness*, ed. J. R. Hamilton and H. Freeman (London: Gaskell Books).

Bourne, S. (1976), 'Second opinion: a study of medical referrals' in a seminar for general practitioners at Tavistock Clinic, London, *Journal of the Royal College of General Practitioners*, vol. 26, pp. 487–95.

Brody, S. and Tarling, R. (1980), *Taking Offenders out of Circulation*, Home Office Research Study no. 64 (London: HMSO).

Butler, Lord (Chairman) (1975), *Report of the Committee on Mentally Abnormal Offenders*, Cmnd 6244 (London: HMSO).

Callahan, E. J. and Leitenberg, H. (1973), 'Aversion therapy for sexual deviation: contingent shock and covert sensitisation', *Journal of Abnormal Psychology*, vol. 81, pp. 60–73.

Cannon, W. B. (1929), *Bodily Changes in Pain, Hunger, Fear and Rage*, 2nd edn (New York: Appleton).

Carruthers, M. (1975), 'Biochemical responses to stress in the environment', *Proceedings of the Royal Society of Medicine*, vol. 68, pp. 429–30.

Cautela, J. R. (1967), 'Covert sensitization', *Psychological Reports*, vol. 20, pp. 459–68.

Cautela, J. R. and Wisocki, P. A. (1971), 'Covert sensitization for the treatment of sexual deviations', *The Psychological Review*, vol. 21, pp. 37–48.

Christie, M. M., Marshall, W. L. and Lanthier, R. D. (1978), *A Descriptive Study of Incarcerated Rapists and Pedophiles*, unpublished monograph.

Clarke, R. V. G. (1977), 'Psychology and crime', *Bulletin of the British Psychological Society*, vol. 30, pp. 280–3.

Clarkson, F. (1978), 'Offences against discipline in a Borstal', *Journal of Adolescence*, vol. 1, pp. 81–7.

Cocozza, J. J. and Steadman, H. J. (1974), 'Some refinements in the measurement and prediction of dangerous behaviour', *American Journal of Psychiatry*, vol. 131, pp. 1012–14.

Cohen, M. L., Garotalo, R., Boucher, R. and Seghorn, T. (1971), *The Psychology of Rapists, Seminars in Psychiatry*, Vol. 3 (New York: Grune & Stratton).

Cohen, S. I. and Silverman, A. J. (1958), 'Psychophysiological investigations of vascular response variability', *Journal of Psychosomatic Research*, vol. 3, pp. 185–210.

Cole, J. O. (1977), 'Research barriers in psychopharmacology', *American Journal of Psychiatry*, vol. 134, no. 8, pp. 896–8.

Como, P. G. (1977), *The Use of Multiple Personality Variables to Predict Recidivism in Prisoners*, unpublished M.A. thesis, University of Texas.

Conrad, J. P. and Dinitz, S. (1977). *In Fear of Each Other* (Lexington, Mass. Toronto: D. C. Heath (Lexington Books)).

Copas, J. B. (1980), *Shrinkage, Prediction and Stepwise Regression*, research report (Salford: University of Salford).

Copas, J. B. and Whiteley, J. S. (1976), 'Predicting success in the treatment of psychopaths', *British Journal of Psychiatry*, vol. 129, pp. 388–92.

Courtenay, M. J. F. (1973), *One Patient, Two Doctors: Six Minutes for the Patient* (London: Tavistock Publications).

Crawford, D. A. (1977), 'The HDHQ results of long-term prisoners: relationships with criminal and institutional behaviour', *British Journal of Social and Clinical Psychology*, vol. 16, no. 4, pp. 391–4.

Crawford, D. A. (1979), 'Modification of deviant sexual behaviour: the need for a comprehensive approach', *British Journal of Medical Psychology*, vol. 52, pp. 151–6.

Crawford, D. A. (1981), 'Treatment approaches with pedophiles', in *Adult Sexual Interest in Children*, ed. M. Cook and K. Howells, (London: Academic Press), pp. 181–217.

Crawford, D. A. and Allen, J. V. (1979), 'A social skills training programme with sex offenders', in *Love and Attraction: Proceedings of an International Conference*, ed. M. Cook and G. Wilson (Oxford: Pergamon Press).

Curtis, E. W. (1971), 'Predictive value compared to predictive validity', *American Psychologist*, vol. 26, pp. 908–14.

Curtis, L. A. (1974), *Criminal Violence: National Patterns and Behavior* (Lexington, Mass: D. C. Heath (Lexington Books)).

Davis, H. M. (1974), 'Psychometric prediction of institutional adjustments: a validated study', *British Journal of Social and Clinical Psychology*, vol. 13, pp. 269–76.

Dell, S. (1980), *The Transfer of Special Hospital Patients to National Health Service Hospitals*, Special Hospitals Research Report no. 16 (London: Special Hospitals Research Unit).

Department of Health and Social Security (1976), *Review of the Mental Health Act, 1959*, Cmnd 7320 (London: HMSO).

Draper, N. R. and Van Nostrand, R. C. (1979), 'Ridge regression and James-Stein estimation: review and comments', *Technometrics*, vol. 21, pp. 451–66.

Dworkin, R. (1977), *Taking Rights Seriously* (London: Duckworth).

Dworkin, R. (1978), 'Philosophy and politics', in *Men of Ideas*, ed. B. Magee (London: British Broadcasting Corporation), pp. 240–60.

Edmunds, G. and Kendrick, D. C. (1980), *The Measurement of Human Aggressiveness* (Chichester: Ellis Horwood).

Ekkers, C. L. (1975), 'Catecholamine excretion, conscience function and aggressive behaviour', *Biological Psychology*, vol. 3, pp. 15–30.

Elmadjian, F., Hope, J. M. and Lamson, E. T. (1957), 'Excretion of epinephrine and norepinephrine in various emotional states', *Journal of Clinical Endocrinology*, vol. 17, pp. 608–20.

Endler, N. S. and Hunt, J. McV. (1968), 'S-R inventories of hostility and comparisons of the proportions of variance from persons, responses and situations for hostility and anxiousness', *Journal of Personality and Social Psychology*, vol. 9, pp. 309–15.

Endler, N. S. and Magnusson, D. (1976), 'Toward an interactional psychology of personality', *Psychological Bulletin*, vol. 83, pp. 956–74.

Ennis, B. J. and Litwack, T. R. (1974), 'Psychiatry and the presumption of expertise: flipping coins in the courtroom', *California Law Review*, vol. 62, pp. 694–752.

Epstein, S. and Taylor, S. P. (1967), 'Instigation to aggression as a function of degree of defeat and perceived aggressive intent of the opponent', *Journal of Personality*, vol. 35, no. 2, pp. 265–89.

Eranko, O. (1955), 'Distribution of adrenaline and noradrenaline in the adrenal medulla', *Nature*, vol. 175, pp. 88–9.

Euler, U. S. von and Lundberg, U. (1954), 'Effects of flying on the epinephrine excretion in air force personnel', *Journal of Applied Physiology*, vol. 6, pp. 551–5.

Farrington, D. P. (1976), 'Statistical prediction methods in criminology', paper delivered at the NATO Advanced Study Institute, Cambridge, July.

Farrington, D. P. (1978), 'The family backgrounds of aggressive youths', in *Aggression and Antisocial Disorder in Children*, ed. L. Hersov, M. Berger and D. Schaffer (London: Pergamon).

Feigelson, E. B., Davis, E. B., McKinnon, R., Schwartz, C. and Shands, H. C. (1978), 'The decision to hospitalize', *American Journal of Psychiatry*, vol. 135, pp. 354–7.

Feldman, M. P. and MacCulloch, M. J. (1965), 'The application of anticipatory avoidance learning to the treatment of homosexuality: I. Theory, technique and preliminary results', *Behaviour Research and Therapy*, vol. 2, pp. 165–83.

Feldman, M. P. and MacCulloch, M. J. (1971), *Homosexual Behaviour: Theory and Assessment* (Oxford: Pergamon Press).

Feldman, M. P., MacCulloch, M. J., Mellor, V. and Pinschof, J. M. (1966), 'The application of anticipatory avoidance learning to the treatment of homosexuality: III. The sexual orientation method', *Behaviour Research and Therapy*, vol. 4, pp. 289–99.

Feshback, S. (1970), 'Aggression', in *Carmichael's Manual of Child Psychology*, Vol. 2, 3rd edn, ed. P. H. Mussen (New York: Wiley).

Fine, B. J. and Sweeney, D. R. (1968), 'Personality traits, situational factors and catecholamine excretion', *Journal of Experimental Research into Personality*, vol. 3, pp. 15–27.

Flor-Henry, P. (1976), 'Lateralized temporal-limbic dysfunction and psychopathology', *Annals of the New York Academy of Sciences*, vol. 280, pp. 777–97.

Folkow, B. and von Euler, U. S. (1954), 'Selective activation of noradrenaline and adrenaline producing cells in the cat's adrenal gland by hypothalamic stimulation', *Circulation Research*, vol. 2, pp. 191–5.

Forster, D. P. and Tiplady, P. (1980), 'Doctors and compulsory procedures: Section 47 of the National Assistance Act 1948', *British Medical Journal*, 8 March, pp. 739–40.

Frankenhaeuser, M. (1971), 'Behaviour and circulating catecholamines', *Brain Research*, vol. 31, pp. 241–62.

Frankenhaeuser, M. and Rissler, A. (1970), 'Effects of punishment on catecholamine release and efficiency of performance', *Psychopharmacology*, vol. 17, pp. 378–90.

Fransella, F. (1972), *Personal Change and Reconstruction: Research on a Treatment of Stuttering* (London: Academic Press).

Fransella, F. and Bannister, D. (1977), *A Manual of Repertory Grid Technique* (London: Academic Press).

Fredericq, L. (1885), 'Influence du milieu ambiant sur la composition du sang des animaux aquatiques', *Archives de Zoologie Expérimentale et Générale*, vol. 3, p. 34.

Freund, K. (1963), 'A laboratory method of diagnosing predominance of homo- or hetero-erotic interest in the male', *Behaviour Research and Therapy*, vol. 1, pp. 85–93.

Freund, K. (1965), 'Diagnosing heterosexual pedophilia by means of a test for sexual interest', *Behaviour Research and Therapy*, vol. 3, pp. 229–34.

Freund, K. (1967), 'Erotic preferences in pedophilia', *Behaviour Research and Therapy*, vol. 5, pp. 339–48.

Freund, K. (1971), 'A note on the use of the phallometric method of measuring mild sexual arousal in the male', *Behaviour Therapy*, vol. 2, pp. 223–8.

Freund, K., Chan, S. and Coulthard, R. (1979), 'Phallometric diagnosis with "non admitters" ', *Behaviour Research and Therapy*, vol. 17, pp. 451–7.

Freund, K. and Costell, R. (1970), 'The structure of erotic preference in the non-deviant male', *Behaviour Research and Therapy*, vol. 8, pp. 15–20.

Freund, K., Langevin, R. and Zajac, Y. (1974), 'A note on the erotic arousal value of moving and stationary forms', *Behaviour Research and Therapy*, vol. 12, pp. 117–19.

Funkenstein, D. H. (1956), 'Norepinephrine and epinephrine-like substances in relation to human behaviour', *Journal of Mental Disease*, vol. 124, pp. 58–68.

Geer, J. H. (1974), 'Cognitive factors in sexual arousal – toward an amalgam of research strategies', paper read at the American Psychological Association, New Orleans, September.

Gellhorn, E. (1965), 'The neurophysiological basis of anxiety, a hypothesis', *Perspectives in Biology and Medicine*, vol. 8, pp. 488–515.

Goldberg, L. R. (1968), 'Simple models or simple processes? Some research on clinical judgements', *American Psychologist*, vol. 23, pp. 483–96.

Goldfried, M. R. and Kent, R. N. (1972), 'Traditional versus behavioural personality assessment: a comparison of methodological and theoretical assumptions', *Psychological Bulletin*, vol. 77, pp. 409–20.

Goodall, McC. (1951), 'Studies of adrenaline and noradrenaline in mammalian heart and suprarenals', *Acta Physiologica Scandinavica*, vol. 24, suppl. 85, pp. 3–57.

Goodall, McC. and Berman, M. L. (1960), 'Urinary output of adrenaline, noradrenaline and 3-methoxy 4 hydroxy mandelic acid following centrifugation and anticipation of centrifugation', *Journal of Clinical Investigation*, vol. 39, p. 1533.

Gordon, A., Marshall, W. L., Loeber, R. and Barbaree, H. E. (1977), 'Toward a definition of social competence in sexual aggressors', paper presented at the First Annual Conference on the Evaluation and Treatment of Sexual Aggressors, Memphis, Tenn., April.

Gough, H. G. (1948), 'A sociological theory of psychopathy', *American Journal of Sociology*, vol. 53, no. 9, pp. 359–66.

Gough, H. G., Wenk, E. A. and Rozynko, V. V. (1965), 'Parole outcome as predicted from CPI, MMPI and a base expectancy table', *Journal of Abnormal Psychology*, vol. 70, pp. 432–41.

Greenwell, J. and Dengerink, H. (1973), 'The role of perceived versus actual attack in human physical aggression', *Journal of Personality and Social Psychology*, vol. 26, no. 1, pp. 66–71.

Hallam, R. S. and Ruchman, S. (1976), 'Current status of aversion theory', in *Progress in Behaviour Modification*, Vol. 2, ed. M. Hersen, R. M. Eisler and P. M. Miller (London: Academic Press).

Hare, R. D. (1968), 'Psychopathy, autonomic functioning and the orienting response', *Journal of Abnormal Psychology*, Monograph Supplement, vol. 73, no. 3, pt 2, pp. 1–24.

Hare, R. D. (1978) 'Electrodermal and cardiovascular correlates of psychopathy', in *Psychiopathic Behaviour: Approaches to Research*, ed. R. D. Hare and D. Schalling (New York: Wiley).

Hare, R. D. (1980), 'Biological and behavioural correlates of criminal psychopathy', in *Lo Psicopatico Delinquente*, Facolta di Giurisprudenza, Universita di Messina (Milan: Giuffre).

Hart, H. L. A. (1955), 'Are there any natural rights?', *Philosophical Review*, vol. 64, pp. 175–91.

Hart, H. L. A. (1968), *Punishment and Responsibility* (Oxford: Clarendon Press).

Hedlund, J. F., Sletten, I. W., Altman, H. and Evenson, R. C. (1973), 'Prediction of patients who are dangerous to others', *Journal of Clinical Psychology*, vol. 29, pp. 443–7.

Heilbrun, A. B. (1979), 'Psychopathy and violent crime', *Journal of Consulting and Clinical Psychology*, vol. 47, pp. 509–16.

Henson, D. E. and Rubin, H. H. (1971), 'Voluntary control of eroticism', *Journal of Applied Behavior Analysis*, vol. 4, pp. 37–44.

Herman, S. H., Barlow, D. H. and Agres, W. S. (1974), 'An experimental analysis of exposure to "elicit" heterosexual stimuli as an effective variable in changing arousal patterns of homosexuals', *Behaviour Research and Therapy*, vol. 12, pp. 335–45.

Herman, S. H. and Prewett, M. (1974), 'An experimental analysis of feedback to increase sexual arousal in a case of homo- and heterosexual impotence: a preliminary report', *Journal of Behavior Therapy and Experimental Psychiatry*, vol. 5, pp. 271–4.

Hillarp, N. A. and Hokfelt, B. (1953), 'Evidence of adrenaline and noradrenaline in separate adrenal medullary cells', *Acta Physiologica Scandinavica*, vol. 30, pp. 55–68.

Hinton, J. W. (1975), *Development of Objective Behaviour Rating Scales for Use by Nurses on Patients in Special Hospitals*, Special Hospitals Research Report no. 13 (London: Special Hospitals Research Unit).

Hinton, J. W. (1977), 'A psychophysiological study of paranoid hostility and defensiveness in maximum security hospital patients', *British Journal of Psychology*, vol. 68, pp. 371–6.

Hinton, J. W. (1978), 'The need for a multi-disciplinary approach to the study of "dangerousness"', paper presented at the Annual Conference of the British Psychological Society, York, April.

Hinton, J. W. (1980), 'Aggression', in *Handbook of Biological Psychiatry*, Vol. 3, ed. H. M. van Praag, M. H. Lader, O. J. Rafaelson and E. J. Sacher (New York: Marcel Dekker), pp. 285–314.

Hinton, J. W. (1981), 'Biological approaches to criminology', in *A Multidisciplinary Approach to Aggression Research*, ed. P. Brain and D. Benton (Amsterdam: ASP Biological and Medical Press, B. V. Elsevier).

Hinton, J. W., O'Neill, M. and Dishman, D. J. (1979), 'Electrodermal indices of public offending and recidivism', *Biological Psychology*, vol. 9, pp. 297–309.

Hinton, J. W., Webster, S. and O'Neill, M. (1978), 'Simple behaviour rating scales for maximum security patients: development and validation', *British Journal of Social and Clinical Psychology*, vol. 17, pp. 255–9.

Hinton, J. W. and Woodman, D. D. (1977), 'Psychophysiological and biochemical characteristics of different types of aggressive offender in a maximum security hospital', paper presented at the Symposium on Psychobiology of Social Deviance, British Psychological Society Conference, Exeter, April.

Holden, A. (1974), *The St. Albans Poisoner* (London: Hodder & Stoughton).

Hollingshead, A. B. and Redlich, F. C. (1958), *Social Class and Mental Illness in a Community Study*, (Chichester: Wiley).

Holmes, W. and Solomon, P. (1980), 'Criteria used in first admissions and readmissions to psychiatric hospitals', *Social Science and Medicine*, vol. 14A, pp. 55–9.

Honderich, T. (1976), *Punishment: The Supposed Justifications*, revised edn (Harmondsworth: Penguin).

Howells, K. (1979a), 'Some meanings of children for pedophiles', in *Love and Attraction*, ed. M. Cook and G. Wilson (Oxford: Pergamon), pp. 519–26.

Howells, K. (1979b), 'The meaning of poisoning to a person diagnosed as a psychopath', *Medicine, Science and the Law*, vol. 8, no. 18, pp. 179–84.

Howells, K. (1981a), 'Images of deviant sexuality', paper presented at the Annual Conference of the British Psychological Society, Sheffield, March.

Howells, K. (1981b), 'Social relationships in violent offenders', in *Personal Relationships in Disorder*, ed. R. Gilmour and S. Duck (London: Academic Press).

Howells, K. and Steadman-Allen, R. (1977), 'The emotional mediation of sexual offences', paper presented to the Annual Conference of the British Psychological Society, Exeter, April.

Howells, K. and Wright, E. (1978), 'The sexual attitudes of aggressive sexual offenders', *British Journal of Criminology*, vol. 18, pp. 170–4.

Hunt, R. C. and Wiley, E. D. (1968), 'Operation Baxstrom after one year', *American Journal of Psychiatry*, vol. 124, pp. 974–8.

Jeffery, C. R. (1974), 'Genetics and criminology: a new look', paper presented at the International Centre of Biological and Medical Legal Criminology, Oscar Freire Institute, Sâo Paulo, Brazil.

Jeffery, C. R. (ed.) (1979), *Biology and Crime* (California, London: Sage Publications).

Jones, E. E., Kanhouse, E., Kelley, H. H., Nisbett, R. E., Valins, S. and Weiner, B. (eds) (1971), *Attribution: Perceiving the Cause of Behavior* (New York: General Learning Press).

Kelly, G. (1955), *The Psychology of Personal Constructs* (New York: Norton).

Klein, J. F. (1976), 'The dangerousness of dangerous offender legislation: forensic folklore revisited', *Canadian Journal of Criminology and Corrections*, vol. 18, pp. 109–22.

Kohlenberg, R. J. (1974), 'Treatment of a homosexual pedophiliac using in vivo desensitization: a case study', *Journal of Abnormal Psychology*, vol. 83, pp. 192–5.

Kozol, H., Boucher, R. and Garofalo, R. (1972), 'The diagnosis and treatment of dangerousness', *Crime and Delinquency*, vol. 18, pp. 371–92.

Kreisman, D. E. and Joy, V. D. (1974), 'Family response to the mental illness of a relative', *Schizophrenia Bulletin*, vol. 10, pp. 34–57.

Krianciunas, R. (1969), 'Age and sex difference in reasons for psychiatric hospitalization', *Gerontologist*, vol. 9, pp. 221–2.

Kvaraceus, W. C. (1966), *Anxious Youth* (Columbus, Ohio: Merrill Books).

Langeluddeke, A. (1963), *Castration of Sexual Criminals* (Berlin: Walter de Gruyter).

Laws, D. R. (1974), 'Non-aversive treatment alternatives of hospitalized pedophiles: an automated fading procedure to alter sexual responsiveness', paper presented at the American Psychological Association, New Orleans, August.

Laws, D. R. (1980), 'The assessment and treatment of sexual offenders', seminar given at the Annual Conference of the British Association for Behavioural Psychotherapy, Sheffield, July.

Laws, D. R. and Rubin, H. H. (1969), 'Instructional control of an autonomic sexual response', *Journal of Applied Behavior Analysis*, vol. 2, pp. 93–9.

Lee-Evans, M. (1978), 'The potential of self control training procedures in the treatment of sex offenders', in *Sex Offenders: A Symposium*, ed J. Gunn, Special Hospitals Research Report no. 14 (London: Special Hospitals Research Unit).

Leon, C. A. and Micklin, M. (1978), 'Who shall be hospitalised? Some social and psychological correlates of alternative dispositions of the mentally ill', *Acta Psychiatrica Scandinavica*, vol. 58, pp. 97–111.

Levi, L. (1972), 'Stress and distress in response to psychosocial stimuli. Laboratory and real life studies on sympathoadrenomedullary and related reactions', *Acta Medica Scandinavica*, suppl. 528, pp. 1–166.

Levine, S. (1962), 'The effects of infantile experience on adult behavior', in

Experimental Foundations of Clinical Psychology, ed. A. J. Bachrach (New York: Basic Books).

Levine, S. (1969), 'An endocrine theory of infantile stimulation', in *Stimulation in Early Infancy*, ed. A. Ambrose (New York: Academic Press).

Lewis, P. S. (1973), 'The prisoner's perception of himself and of his world', Ph.D. thesis, University of Leeds.

Lukes, S. (1973), *Individualism* (Oxford: Blackwell).

Lund, A. (1949), 'Fluorimetric determination of adrenaline in blood', *Acta Pharmacologia*, vol. 5, pp. 231–47.

Maccoby, E. E., Gibbs, P. K. and the Staff of the Laboratory of Human Development, Harvard University (1954), 'Methods of child rearing in two social classes', in *Readings in Child Development*, ed. W. E. Martin and C. B. Stendler (New York: Harcourt Brace Jovanovitch), pp. 380–96.

McConaghy, N. (1969), 'Subjective and penile plethysmograph responses following aversion-relief and apomorphine aversion therapy for homosexual impulses', *British Journal of Psychiatry*, vol. 115, pp. 723–30.

McGarry, A. L. and Parker, L. L. (1974), 'Massachusetts' operation Baxstrom: a follow-up', *Massachusetts Journal of Mental Health*, vol. 4, pp. 27–41.

McGuire, R. J., Carlisle, J. M. and Young, B. G. (1965), 'Sexual deviations as conditioned behaviour', *Behaviour Research and Therapy*, vol. 2, pp. 185–90.

McGurk, B. J. (1978), 'Personality types among "normal" homicides', *British Journal of Criminology*, vol. 18, pp. 146–61.

McGurk, B. J. and McGurk, R. E. (1979), 'Personality types among prisoners and prison officers', *British Journal of Criminology*, vol. 19, no. 1, pp. 31–49.

Mack, J. L. (1969), 'Behaviour ratings of recidivist and non-recidivist delinquent males', *Psychological Reports*, vol. 25, p. 260.

Mannheim, H. and Wilkins, L. T. (1955), *Prediction Methods in Relation to Borstal Training* (London: HMSO).

Marquis, J. (1970), 'Orgasmic reconditioning: changing sexual object choice through controlling masturbation fantasies', *Journal of Behavior Therapy and Experimental Psychiatry*, vol. 1, pp. 263–71.

Marshall, W. L. (1973), 'The modification of sexual fantasies: a combined treatment approach to the reduction of deviant sexual behaviour', *Behaviour Research and Therapy*, vol. 11, pp. 557–64.

Marshall, W. L. and Barbaree, H. E. (1978), 'The reduction of deviant arousal: satiation treatment for sexual aggressors', *Criminal Justice and Behavior*, vol. 5, pp. 294–303.

Marshall, W. L. and McKnight, R. D. (1975), 'An integrated treatment programme for sexual offenders', *Canadian Psychiatric Association Journal*, vol. 20, pp. 133–8.

Marshall, W. L., Williams, S. M. and Christie, M. M. (1977), 'The treatment of rapists', in *Perspectives on Rape*, ed. C. B. Qualls (New York: Pergamon).

Matthews, R. (1977), 'Assessment of sexual offenders at Wormwood Scrubs', paper presented at the Annual Conference of the British Psychological Society, Exeter, April.

Maxwell, A. E. (1977), *Multivariate Analysis in Behavioural Research* (London: Chapman & Hall).

Mednick, S. A. (1975), 'Autonomic nervous system recovery and psychopathy', *Scandinavian Journal of Behaviour Therapy*, vol. 5, pp. 55–68.

Megargee, E. I. (1966), 'Undercontrolled and overcontrolled personality types in extreme antisocial aggression', *Psychological Monographs*, vol. 80, pt 3, no. 611.

Megargee, E. I. (1970), 'The prediction of violence with psychological tests', in *Current Topics in Clinical and Community Psychology*, Vol. 2, ed. C. D. Spielberger (New York: Academic Press).

Megargee, E. I. (1971), 'The role of inhibition in the assessment and understanding of violence', in *The Control of Aggression and Violence: Cognitive and Physiological Factors*, ed. J. E. Singer (London: Academic Press), pp. 125–47.

Megargee, E. I. (1976), 'The prediction of dangerous behaviour', *Criminal Justice and Behavior*, vol. 3, no. 1, pp. 3–22.

Megargee, E. I. and Menzies, E. S. (1971), 'The assessment and dynamics of aggression', in *Advances in Psychological Assessment*, Vol. 2, ed. P. McReynolds (Palo Alto: Science & Behavior Books).

Mendel, W. M. and Rapport, S. (1969), 'Determinants of the decision for psychiatric hospitalisation', *Archives of General Psychiatry*, vol. 20, pp. 321–8.

Miller, K. S., Simons, R. L. and Fein, S. B. (1974), 'Compulsory mental hospitalisation in England and Wales', *Journal of Health and Social Behaviour*, vol. 15, pp. 151–6.

Mischel, W. (1968), *Personality and Assessment* (New York: Wiley).

Mischel, W. (1969), *Towards a Reconceptualization of Personality*, unpublished monograph, Stanford University.

Mischel, W. (1973), 'Toward a cognitive social learning reconceptualisation of personality', *Psychological Review*, vol. 80, pp. 252–83.

Mischel, W. (1977), 'The interaction of person and situation', in *Personality at the Cross Roads*, ed. D. Magnusson and N. S. Endler (Hillsdale: Erlbaum).

Mischler, E. G. and Waxler, N. E. (1963), 'Decision making processes in psychiatric hospitalization: patients referred, accepted and admitted to psychiatric hospital', *American Sociological Review*, vol. 28, pp. 276–87.

Molof, M. J. (1967), *Differences between Assaultive and Non-Assaultive Juvenile Offenders in the California Youth Authority*, California Department of Youth Authority, Division of Research, Report no. 41 (Sacramento: California Department of Youth Authority).

Monahan, J. (1976), 'The prevention of violence', in *Community Mental Health and the Criminal Justice System*, ed. J. Monahan (New York: Pergamon).

Monahan, J. (1978), 'The prediction of violent criminal behaviour: a methodological critique and prospectus', in *Deterrence and Incapacitation: Estimating the Effects of Criminal Sanctions on Crime Rates*, ed. A. Blumstein, J. Cohen and D. Nagin (Washington, DC: National Academy of Sciences), pp. 244–69.

Morris, T. and Morris, P. (1961), 'The experience of imprisonment', *British Journal of Criminology*, vol. 2, pp. 337–60.

Morris, T. and Morris, P. (1963), *Pentonville* (London: Routledge & Kegan Paul).

Muir Gray, J. A. (1930), 'Section 47: an ethical dilemma for doctors', *Health Trends*, vol. 12, pp. 372–4.

Nickel, T. W. (1974), 'The attribution of intention as a critical factor in the relation between frustration and aggression', *Journal of Personality*, vol. 42, no. 3, pp. 482–92.

Nie, N. H., Bent, D. H. and Hull, C. H. (1970), *Statistical Package for the Social Sciences* (New York: McGraw-Hill).

Norris, M. (1977), 'Construing in a detention centre', in *New Perspectives in Personal Construct Theory*, ed. D. Bannister (London: Academic Press).

Novaco, R. W. (1978), 'Anger and coping with stress', in *Cognitive Behavior Therapy*, ed. J. P. Foreyt and D. P. Rathjen (New York: Plenum Press), pp. 135–73.

Nuttall, C. (1977), *Parole in England and Wales*, Home Office Research Study no. 38 (London: HMSO).

Olweus, D. (1973), 'Personality and Aggression', in *Nebraska Symposium on Motivation*, ed. J. K. Cole and D. D. Jensen (Lincoln, Nebr.: University of Nebraska Press).

Olweus, D. (1979), 'Stability of aggressive reaction patterns in males: a review', *Psychological Bulletin*, vol. 86, pp. 852–75.

Olweus, D. (1980), 'The consistency issue in personality psychology revisited: with special reference to aggression', *British Journal of Social and Clinical Psychology*, vol. 19, pp. 377–90.

Osgood, C. E., Suci, G. J. and Tannenbaum, P. H. (1957), *The Measurement of Meaning* (Urbana, Ill.: University of Illinois Press).

Pacht, A. R. (1976), 'The rapist in treatment: professional myths', in *Sexual Assault*, ed. M. J. Walker and S. L. Brodsky (Lexington, Mass.: D. C. Heath (Lexington Books)), pp. 91–8.

Perkins, D. E. (1977), 'Development of a treatment programme for sexual offenders in a prison setting', paper presented at the Annual Conference of the British Psychological Society, Exeter, April.

Pfohl, S. (1977), 'The psychiatric assessment of dangerousness: practical problems and political implications', in *In Fear of Each Other*, ed. J. P. Conrad and S. Dinitz (Lexington, Mass./Toronto: D. C. Heath (Lexington Books)).

Quinsey, V. L., Warneford, A., Pruesse, M. and Link, N. (1975). 'Released Oak Ridge patients: a follow-up study of review board discharges', *British Journal of Criminology*, vol. 15, pp. 264–70.

Quinton, A. (1973), *Utilitarian Ethics* (London: Macmillan).

Radzinowicz, L. and Hood, R. (1978), 'A dangerous direction for sentencing reform', *Criminal Law Review*, pp. 713–24.

Rawls, J. (1972), *A Theory of Justice* (London: OUP).

Redgate, E. S. and Gellhorn, E. (1953), 'Nature of sympathico-adrenal discharge under conditions of excitation of central autonomic structures', *American Journal of Physiology*, vol. 174, pp. 475–80.

Report of the Committee appointed to enquire into the pathology and treatment of the venereal disease, with a view to diminishing its injurious effects upon the men of the army and navy; with appendices and evidence (1867–8), *Parliamentary Papers*, vol. XXXVII (4031), p. 425.

Report of the Review of Rampton Hospital (1980), Rampton Hospital Management Review Team: Sir J. Boynton (Ch.), DHSS, Cmnd 8073 (London: HMSO).

Report of the Royal Commission on the Law relating to Mental Illness and Mental Deficiency, The Rt Hon. The Lord Percy of Newcastle (1954), Cmd 9212 (London: HMSO).

Report of the Royal Commissioners on the Care and Control of the Feeble-minded (1908), Cd 4202 (London: HMSO).

Revitch, E. and Schlesinger, B. (1978), 'Murder: evaluation, classification and prediction', in *Violence: Perspectives on Murder and Aggression*, ed. I. L. Kutash, S. B. Kutash, L. B. Schlesinger and Associates (San Francisco: Jossey-Bass).

Rubin, B. (1972), 'The prediction of dangerousness in mentally ill criminals', *Archives of General Psychiatry*, vol. 27, pp. 397–407.

Rushing, W. A. (1969), 'Two patterns in the relationship between social class and mental hospitalization', *American Sociological Review*, vol. 34, pp. 533–41.

Sapsford, R. (1979), *Life-Sentence Prisoners: Deterioration and Coping* (Milton Keynes: The Open University, Social Science Publications).

Sarbin, T. (1967), 'The dangerous individual: an outcome of social identity transformations', *British Journal of Criminology*, vol. 7, no. 3, pp. 285–95.

Scarpetti, W. L. (1974), 'Autonomic concomitants of aggressive behaviour in repressors and sensitisers: a social learning approach', *Journal of Personality and Social Psychology*, vol. 30, pp. 772–81.

Schachter, S. and Singer, J. E. (1962), 'Cognitive, social and physiological determinants of emotional state', *Psychological Review*, vol. 69, pp. 379–99.

Schalling, D. (1978), 'Psychopathy related personality variables and the psychophysiology of socialization', in *Psychopathic Behaviour: Approaches to Research*, ed. R. D. Hare and D. Schalling (New York: Wiley).

Scottish Council on Crime (1975), *Crime and the Prevention of Crime* (Edinburgh: HMSO).

Seligman, M. E. P. (1975), *Helplessness* (San Francisco: Freeman).

Selye, H. (1936), 'A syndrome produced by diverse nocuous agents', *Nature*, vol. 128, p. 32.

Serber, M. (1970), 'Shame aversion therapy', *Journal of Behaviour Therapy and Experimental Psychiatry*, vol. 1, pp. 217–26.

Serber, M. and Wolpe, J. (1972), 'Behaviour therapy techniques', in *Sexual Behaviour*, ed. H. L. P. Resnick and M. E. Wolfgang (Boston, Mass.: Little, Brown), pp. 239–54.

Shah, S. A. (1978), 'Dangerousness: a paradigm for exploring some issues in law and psychology', *American Psychologist*, vol. 33, pp. 224–38.

Simon, F. H. (1971), *Prediction Methods in Criminology* (London: HMSO).

Slater, P. (1972), 'Notes on Ingrid "72" ', unpublished manuscript, St George's Hospital.

Slater, P. (1976), *The Measurement of Intrapersonal Space by Grid Technique*, Vol. 1: *Exploration of Intrapersonal Space* (London: Wiley).

Slater, P. (1977), *The Measurement of Intrapersonal Space by Grid Technique*, Vol. 2: *Dimensions of Intrapersonal Space* (London: Wiley).

Sluga, W. (1977), 'Treatment of long-term prisoners considered from the medical and psychiatric point of view', in *Treatment of Long-Term Prisoners* (Strasburg: Council of Europe).

Smith, K., Pomphrey, M. W. and Hall, J. C. (1963), 'The "last straw": the decisive incident resulting in the request for hospitalization in 100 schizophrenic patients', *American Journal of Psychiatry*, vol. 120, pp. 228–33.

Steadman, H. J. (1973), 'Some evidence on the inadequacy of the concept and determination of dangerousness in law and psychiatry', *Journal of Psychiatry and Law*, vol. 1, pp. 409–26.

Steadman, H. J. and Cocozza, J. J. (1974), *Careers of the Criminally Insane* (Lexington, Mass.: D. C. Heath (Lexington Books)).

Stein, C. (1960), 'Multiple regression', in *Contributions to Probability and Statistics in Honour of Harold Hottelling*, ed. I. Olkin (Stanford: Stanford University Press), pp. 424–43.

Stone, M. (1974), 'Cross validatory choice and assessment of statistical predictions', *Journal of the Royal Statistical Society*, Series B, vol. 36, pp. 111–47.

Storms, M. D. and McCaul, K. D. (1976), 'Attribution processes and emotional excerbation of dysfunctional behavior', in *New Directions in Attribution Research*, Vol. 1, ed. J. H. Harvey, W. J. Ickes and R. F. Kidd (Hillsdale: Erlbaum), pp. 143–64.

Stürup, G. (1968), *Treatment of Sexual Offenders in Herstedvester, Denmark: The Rapists* (Copenhagen: Munsgard).

Stürup, G. (1972), 'Castration: the total treatment', in *Sexual Behaviour*, ed. H. L. P. Resnick and M. F. Wolfgang (Boston, Mass.: Little, Brown).

Taggart, P., Gibbons, D. and Somerville W. (1969), 'Some effects of motor car driving on the normal and abnormal heart', *British Medical Journal*, vol. 4, pp. 130–4.

Tanner, B. A. (1974), 'A comparison of automated aversion conditioning and a waiting list control in the modification of homosexual behaviour in males', *Behaviour Therapy*, vol. 5, pp. 29–32.

Taylor, S. P. (1967), 'Aggressive behaviour and physiological arousal as a function of provocation and the tendency to inhibit aggression', *Journal of Personality*, vol. 35, pp. 297–310.

Tennent, T. G. (1971), 'The dangerous offender', *British Journal of Hospital Medicine*, September, pp. 269–74.

Thorpe, J., Schmidt, G. and Castell, D. (1963), 'A comparison of positive and negative (aversive) conditioning in the treatment of homosexuality', *Behaviour Research and Therapy*, vol. 1, pp. 357–62.

Tong, J. E. (1959), 'Stress reactivity in relation to delinquent and psychopathic behaviour', *Journal of Mental Science*, vol. 105, pp. 935–56.

Topcu, S. (1976), 'Psychological concomitants of aggressive feelings and behaviour', Ph.D. thesis, University of London.

Trasler, G. B. (1962), *The Explanation of Criminality* (London: Routledge & Kegan Paul).

Treves Brown, C. (1977), 'Who is the psychopath?', *Medicine, Science and the Law*, vol. 17, no. 1, pp. 56–63.

Turpin, J. P., Mahar, D. and Smith, D. (1973), 'Two types of violent offenders with psychological descriptors', *Diseases of the Nervous System*, vol. 34, pp. 356–63.

Valins, S. and Nisbett, R. E. (1971), 'Attribution processes in the development and treatment of emotional disorders', in *Attribution: Perceiving the Cause of Behaviour*, ed. E. E. Jones, D. Kanouse, H. H. Kelley, R. E. Nisbett, S. Valins and B. Weiner (New York: General Learning Press).

Venables, P. H. (1977), 'The electrodermal psychophysiology of schizophrenics and children at risk for schizophrenia: current controversies and developments', *Schizophrenia Bulletin*, vol. 3, pp. 28–48.

Walker, N. (1978), 'Dangerous people', *International Journal of Law and Psychiatry*, vol. 1, pp. 37–49.

Walker, N. (1980), *Punishment, Danger and Stigma* (Oxford: Blackwell).

Walker, N. D. (1969), *Sentencing in a Rational Society* (London: Penguin).

Walker, N. D., Hammond, W. and Steer, D. (1967), 'Repeated violence', in *Criminal Law Review*, pp. 465–72.

Waxler, N. E. and Mischler, E. G. (1963), 'Hospitalisation of psychiatric patients: physician centred and family centred influence patterns', *Journal of Health and Human Social Behaviour*, vol. 4, pp. 250–7.

Weil-Malherbe, H. and Bone, A. D. (1952), 'The chemical estimation of adrenaline like substances in blood', *Biochemical Journal*, vol. 51, pp. 311–18.

Welch, A. S. and Welch, B. L. (1971), 'Isolation, reactivity and aggression: evidence for the involvement of brain catecholamines and serotonin', in *The Physiology of Aggression and Defeat*, ed. B. Eleftheriou and J. P. Scott (New York: Plenum Press).

Wenk, E. A., Robinson, J. O. and Smith, G. B. (1972), 'Can violence be predicted?', *Crime and Delinquency*, vol. 18, pp. 393–402.

Widom, C. S. (1976), 'Interpersonal and personal construct systems in psychopaths', *Journal of Consulting and Clinical Psychology*, vol. 44, no. 4, pp. 614–23.

Widom, C. S. (1978), 'An empirical classification of female offenders', *Criminal Justice and Behavior*, vol. 5, no. 1, pp. 35–52.

Wilkins, L. T. (1962), 'What is prediction and is it necessary in evaluating treatment?', in *The Sociology of Crime and Delinquency*, ed. M. E. Wolfgang, L. Savitz and N. Johnston (New York: Wiley), p. 99.

Wing, J. K. (1971), 'International comparisons in the study of the functional psychoses', *British Medical Bulletin*, vol. 27, no. 1, pp. 77–82.

Woodman, D. D. (1979a) 'Evidence of a permanent imbalance in catecholamine secretion in violent social deviants', *Journal of Psychosomatic Research*, vol. 23, pp. 155–7.

Woodman, D. D. (1979b), 'Urinary catecholamines and test habituation in maximum security hospital patients', *Journal of Psychosomatic Research*, vol. 23, pp. 263–6.

Woodman, D. D. and Hinton, J. W. (1978a), 'Anomalies of cyclic AMP excretion in some abnormal offenders', *Biological Psychology*, vol. 7, pp. 103–8.

Woodman, D. D. and Hinton, J. W. (1978b), 'Catecholamine balance during stress anticipation', *Journal of Psychosomatic Research*, vol. 22, pp. 477–83.

Woodman, D. D., Hinton, J. W. and O'Neill, M. T. (1978a), 'Plasma catecholamines, stress and aggression in maximum security patients', *Biological Psychology*, vol. 6, pp. 147–54.

Woodman, D. D., Hinton, J. W. and O'Neill, M. T. (1978b), 'Cortisol secretion and stress in maximum security hospital patients', *Journal of Psychosomatic Research*, vol. 22, pp. 133–6.

Woodward, R. (1980), *Brief Report on the Effects of Sex Education Course on Borstal Trainees*, Home Office Prison Department Psychological Services DPS Reports, Series II, no. 78 (London: Home Office Prison Department).

Yeudall, L. T. (1977), 'Neuropsychological assessment of forensic disorders', *Canada's Mental Health*, vol. 25, pp. 7–15.

Zillman, D. (1979), *Hostility and Aggression* (Hillsdale: Erlbaum).

Zuckerman, M. (1971), 'Physiological measures of sexual arousal in the human', *Psychological Bulletin*, vol. 75, pp. 279–329.

Index

Numbers in italics indicate figures within the text